Intermediate A Mathematics

Nancy L. McGraw

Bright Ideas Press, LLC
Cleveland, Ohio

Simple Solutions Intermediate A

Printed in the United States of America

ISBN-13: 978-1-934210-12-3
ISBN-10: 1-934210-12-9

Cover Design: Dan Mazzola
Editor: Kimberly A. Dambrogio

Welcome to Simple Solutions

Note to the Student:

This workbook will give you the opportunity to practice skills you have learned in previous grades. By practicing these skills each night, you will gain confidence in your math ability.

Using this workbook will help you understand math concepts easier and for many of you, it will give you a more positive attitude toward math in general.

In order for this program to help you be successful, it is extremely important that you do every lesson every night. It is also important that you ask your teacher for help on the problems you don't understand or get wrong when checking your homework.

If you put forth the effort, we guarantee that Simple Solutions will change your opinion about math forever.

Lesson #1

1. How many teaspoons are in a tablespoon?

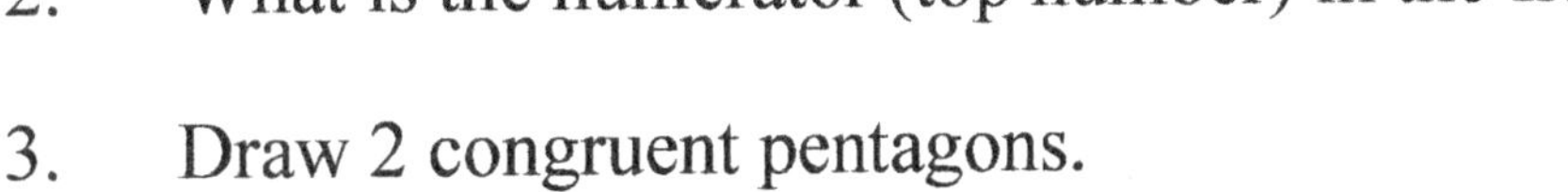

2. What is the numerator (top number) in the fraction $\frac{2}{5}$?

3. Draw 2 congruent pentagons.

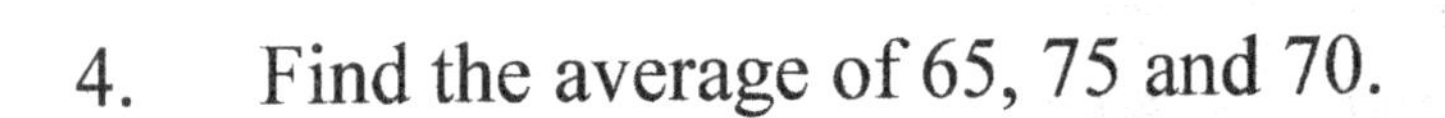

4. Find the average of 65, 75 and 70.

5. It is 7:15. What time was it six hours ago?

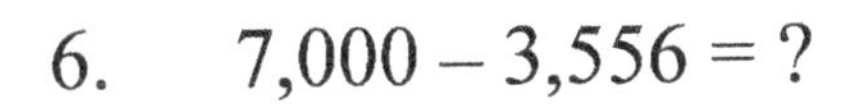

6. 7,000 – 3,556 = ?

7. How many feet are in a mile?

8. Which is greater, 900 lbs. or 1 ton?

9. 6,524 × 6 = ?

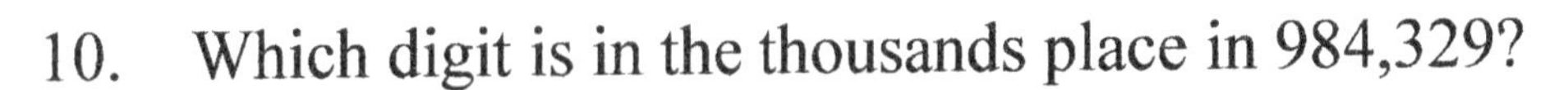

10. Which digit is in the thousands place in 984,329?

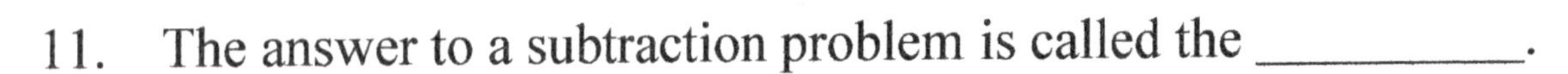

11. The answer to a subtraction problem is called the __________.

12. 3,656 ÷ 6 = ?

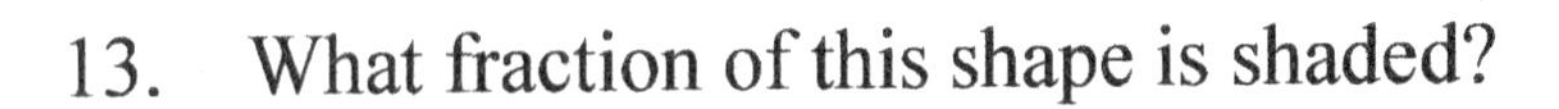

13. What fraction of this shape is shaded?

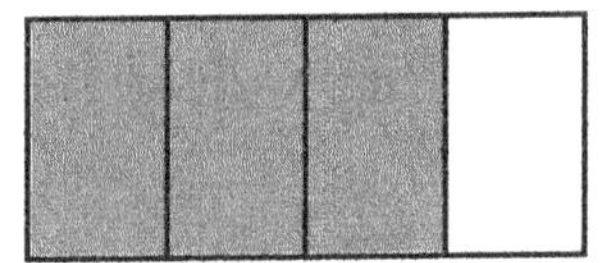

14. Draw intersecting lines.

15. 35 × 23 = ?

16. 845,677 + 336,907 = ?

17. Round 66,485 to the nearest ten thousand.

18. Write the next number in the sequence. 46, 51, 56, …

19. The soccer team has won 30 trophies. Kelvon wants to put the trophies on shelves. If he puts 5 trophies on each shelf, which equation can be used to find the number of shelves he will need?

    A) $30 \times 5 = n$ B) $30 \div 5 = n$

20. List the even numbers between 61 and 69.

1.	2.	3.	4.
5.	6.	7.	8.
9.	10.	11.	12.
13.	14.	15.	16.
17.	18.	19.	20.

Lesson #2

1. How many quarts are in 7 gallons?

2. \$57.34 + \$18.55 = ?

3. Write 9,478 in expanded form.

4. **The range is the difference between the largest value and the smallest value.** Find the range of 96, 28, 35, 77 and 19.

5. Would a CD best be weighed in ounces or in pounds?

6. $5,218 \times 4 = ?$

7. $584,325 + 297,039 = ?$

8. From December 5 to March 5 is how many months?

9. $905 \div 5 = ?$

10. $871 - 299 = ?$

11. Round 7,215,933 to the nearest thousand.

12. The answer to a division problem is called the ________.

13. 7,762 ◯ 7,672

14. Hank bought 6 tickets to the concert. Each ticket cost \$7.95. How much did Hank spend?

15. Write the decimal eight and four tenths.

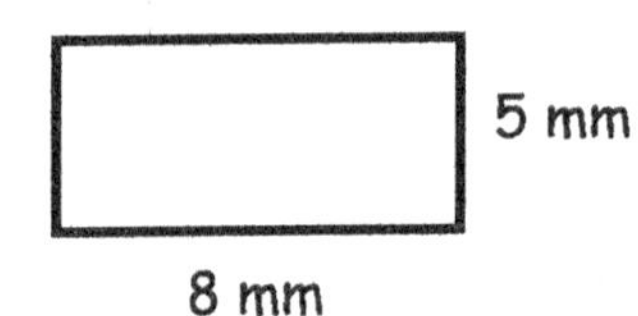

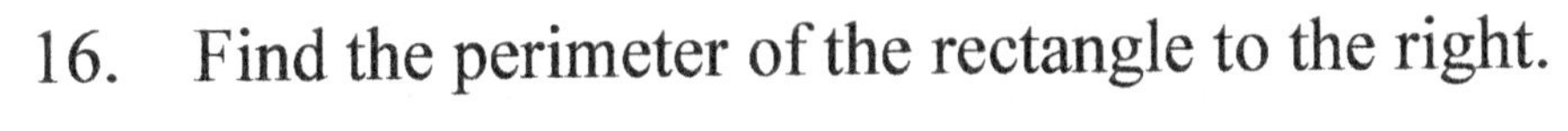

16. Find the perimeter of the rectangle to the right.

17. Would a city bus weigh about 300 pounds or 3 tons?

18. The top number in a fraction is called the ___________.

19. How many quarters are in four dollars?

20. Identify the type of angle.

1.	2.	3.	4.
5.	6.	7.	8.
9.	10.	11.	12.
13.	14.	15.	16.
17.	18.	19.	20.

Lesson #3

1. Give the name of this shape.

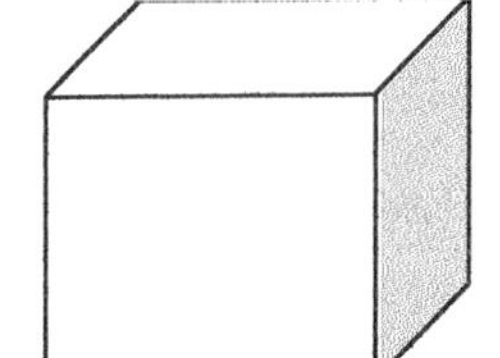

2. 12 × 12 = ?
3. \$34.22 + \$29.94 = ?
4. Write the next number in the sequence. 57, 64, 71, …
5. What year was two decades before 1965?
6. Which digit is in the hundred thousands place in 841,536?
7. How many grams are in a kilogram?
8. Find the perimeter of this figure.

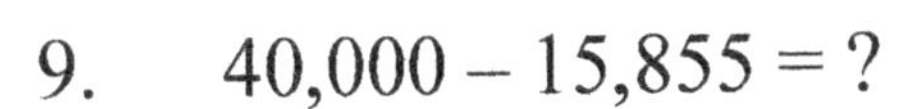

9. 40,000 – 15,855 = ?

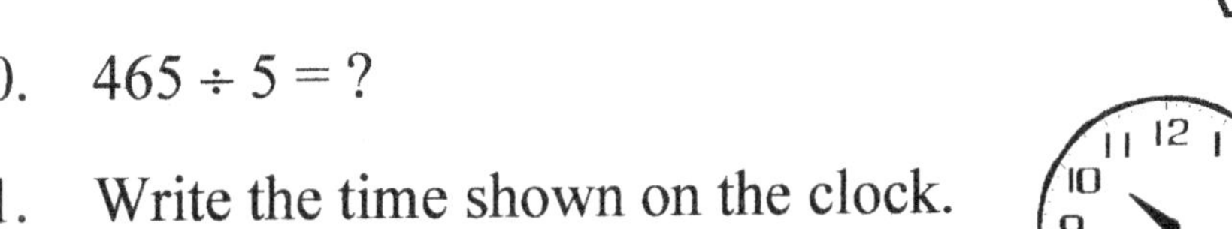

10. 465 ÷ 5 = ?
11. Write the time shown on the clock.

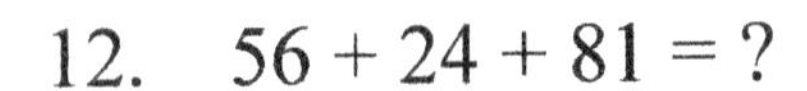

12. 56 + 24 + 81 = ?
13. Is the length of a car about 10 feet or 10 inches?
14. If the diameter of a circle is 18 mm, what is the radius?
15. Write the standard number for 70,000 + 2,000 + 500 + 70 + 3.
16. Find the average of 11, 87 and 19.
17. Draw a hexagon.
18. What is the bottom number in a fraction called?
19. Kelly is 3 years older than Mario. Mario is 4 years younger than Gloria. Gloria is 15. How old is Kelly?
20. 45,987 ◯ 48,999

1.	2.	3.	4.
5.	6.	7.	8.
9.	10.	11.	12.
13.	14.	15.	16.
17.	18.	19.	20.

Lesson #4

1. $8{,}490 \div 3 = ?$

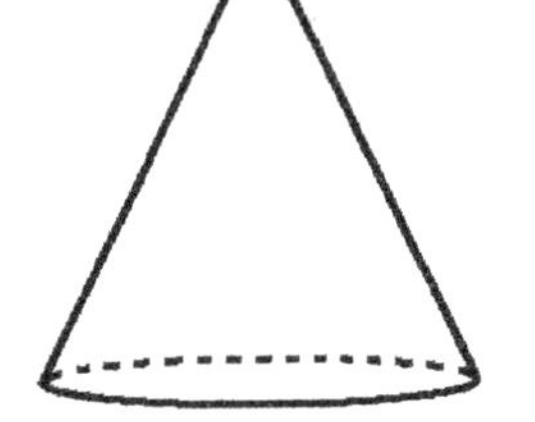

2. How many ounces are in 5 pounds?

3. Round 5,327,408 to the nearest million.

4. Write the name of this solid.

5. **The median is the middle number when all of the numbers are arranged in order.** Find the median of 45, 12, 31, 59 and 11.

6. $965 \div 4 = ?$

7. The top number in a fraction is called the ________________.

8. How many yards are in a mile?

9. $5{,}680 \times 4 = ?$

10. A closed figure made up of line segments is called a(n) __________.

11. Find the perimeter of the triangle shown here.

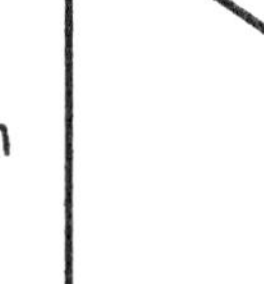

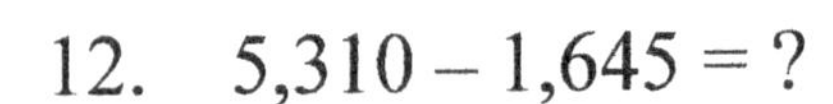

12. $5{,}310 - 1{,}645 = ?$

13. How many nickels are in $2?

14. Draw a vertical line segment.

15. It is 4:00. What time was it 3 hours and 15 minutes ago?

16. What fraction is shaded?

17. Draw an acute angle.

18. Does a bowl weigh about 75 grams or 75 kilograms?

19. The answer in a multiplication problem is called the ______________.

20. Marissa bought 6 pens and gave away 3 pens. Then she bought 4 more pens and lost 2 pens. After buying 5 more pens, Marissa had 25 pens. How many pens did Marissa start with? Explain how you got your answer.

1.	2.	3.	4.
5.	6.	7.	8.
9.	10.	11.	12.
13.	14.	15.	16.
17.	18.	19.	20.

Lesson #5

1. How many cups are in 5 pints?

2. $79 + 38 + 27 = ?$

3. $32 \times 15 = ?$

4. Write the next number in the sequence. 66, 74, 82, …

5. If the radius of a circle is 14 cm, what is the diameter?

6. Draw a ray.

7. Round 789,132 to the nearest ten thousand.

8. Find the average of 160, 121 and 151.

9. $936 \div 8 = ?$

10. Draw a right angle.

11. $900 - 453 = ?$

12. The amusement park has two water rides. Each hour 1,250 people can ride on one of the water rides and 1,325 people can ride the other water ride. If both water rides are filled for 5 hours, find the total number of riders.

13. A four-sided polygon is called a(n) ______________.

8 m

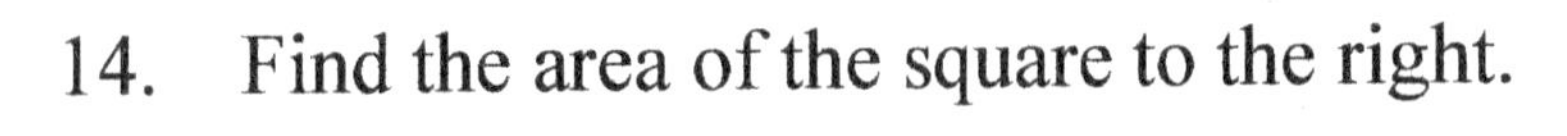

14. Find the area of the square to the right.

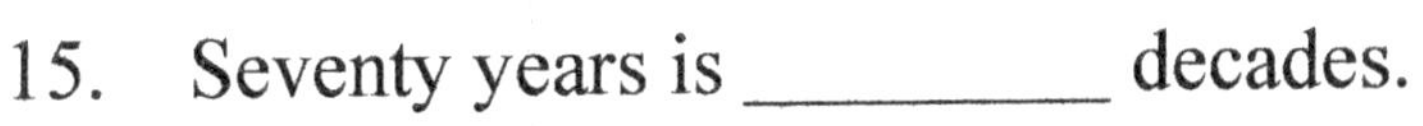

15. Seventy years is __________ decades.

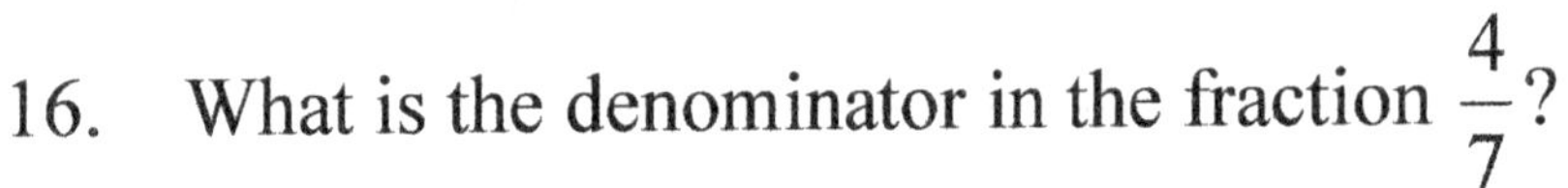

16. What is the denominator in the fraction $\frac{4}{7}$?

17. Write the odd numbers between 50 and 58.

18. $9 \times 8 = ?$

19. What is the probability of rolling a 4 on one roll of a die?

20. Nikki has 5 quarters, 3 dimes and 3 nickels. How much money does she have?

1.	2.	3.	4.
5.	6.	7.	8.
9.	10.	11.	12.
13.	14.	15.	16.
17.	18.	19.	20.

Lesson #6

1. Round 6,789,356 to the nearest million.

2. The sum is the answer to a(n) ____________ problem.

3. The bottom number in a fraction is called the ____________.

4. Draw a line segment.

5. Find the range of 88, 11, 56, 63 and 7.

6. Figures with the same size and shape are ____________.

7. Write the even numbers between 51 and 59.

8. Name the shape.

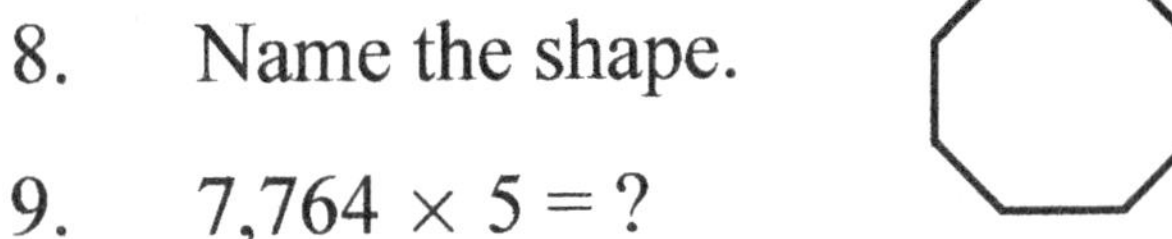

9. $7,764 \times 5 = ?$

10. Write 621,973 in expanded form.

11. Would a penny weigh about a gram or a kilogram?

12. $66,056 \div 4 = ?$

13. 800 years are how many centuries?

14. **There are 1,000 millimeters in 1 meter.**
    Write *1,000 mm = 1 m* three times.

15. What is the probability of getting heads on one flip of a coin?

16. How many teaspoons are in 7 tablespoons?

17. Find the average of 60, 75, 88 and 93.

18. $500 \div 25 = ?$

19. $216,779 + 189,542 = ?$

20. Brooke is on a diet. Each month she records her weight in pounds. If the weights form a pattern, what is the missing weight?

Month	Weight
April	179
May	167
June	???
July	143

1.	2.	3.	4.
5.	6.	7.	8.
9.	10.	11.	12.
13.	14.	15.	16.
17.	18.	19.	20.

Lesson #7

1. $8 \times 8 = ?$

2. $456 \div 16 = ?$

3. Find the perimeter and area of the rectangle.

4. $4{,}566 + 8{,}739 = ?$

5. Draw 2 circles that are similar.

6. Round 3,572,089 to the nearest million.

7. $22 \times 31 = ?$

8. How many yards are in a mile?

9. Write the name of this figure.

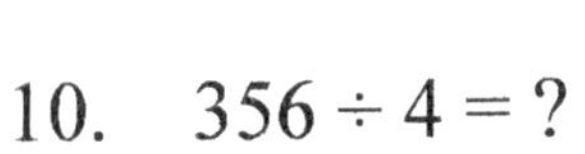

10. $356 \div 4 = ?$

11. Write the fraction that is greater.

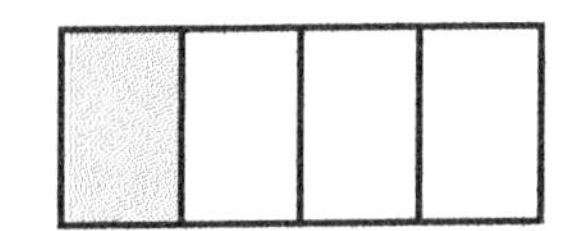
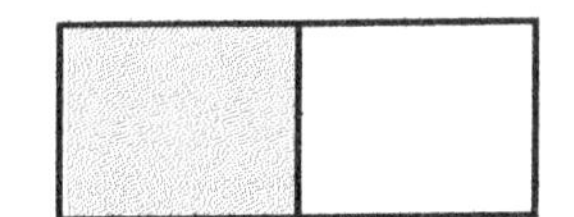

12. $600 - 234 = ?$

13. Find the median of 11, 99, 62, 30 and 41.

14. If it is 11:30 now, what time will it be in 3 hours and 10 minutes?

15. Which digit is in the hundred thousands place in 7,809,112?

16. Estimate the product of 45 and 23.

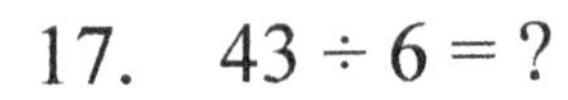

17. $43 \div 6 = ?$

18. 1,235 ○ 1,352

19. $77 + \_\_\_\_ = 90$

20. Wendy bought 8 boxes of candy. She paid $1.50 for each box. She wants to sell the boxes of candy for $2.75 each. Wendy would like to make a profit of at least $8. If she sells 6 of the 8 boxes of candy, will she reach her goal? Explain how you got your answer.

1.	2.	3.	4.
5.	6.	7.	8.
9.	10.	11.	12.
13.	14.	15.	16.
17.	18.	19.	20.

Lesson #8

1. How many millimeters are in a meter?

2. \$45.66 + \$19.03 = ?

3. Determine the area of this figure.

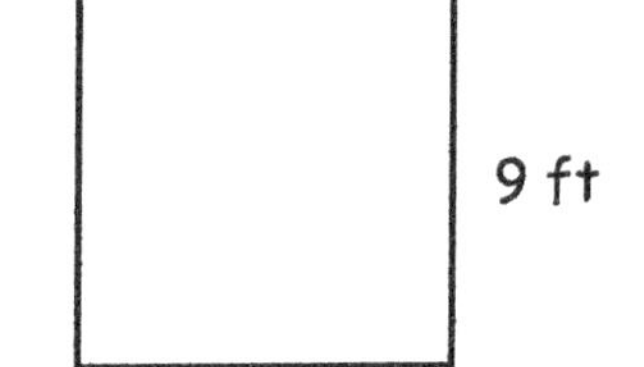

4. 7,132 – 1,966 = ?

5. The distance across a circle, through the center, is the __________.

6. Which digit is in the ten thousands place in 7,908,214?

7. Write the standard number for 90,000 + 8,000 + 600 + 70.

8. What is the probability of rolling a 2 on one roll of a die?

9. A quadrilateral has _______ sides.

10. Draw perpendicular lines.

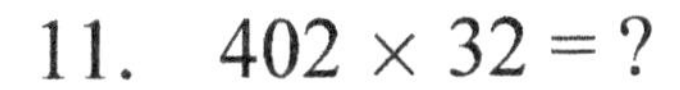

11. 402 × 32 = ?

12. 9,325 ÷ 5 = ?

13. Any number multiplied by zero is equal to __________.

14. Write the next two numbers in the sequence. 46, 54, 62, …

15. If a truck weighs 6 tons, how many pounds does it weigh?

16. Round 8,786,215 to the nearest hundred.

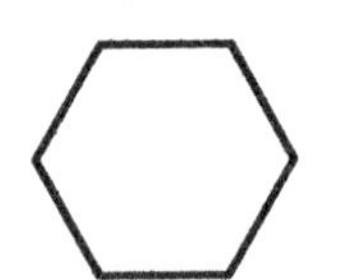

17. What is the name of the shape to the right?

18. An angle that measures less than 90° is called a(n) _________ angle.

19. **A straight angle is a line. Its measure is 180°.** Draw a straight angle and label it 180°.

20. Jason bowled four games at a cost of \$2.50 per game. He rented shoes for \$1.75, and he bought a pizza for \$5.25. He had a coupon for \$1 off per game. How much did Jason spend in all?

1.	2.	3.	4.
5.	6.	7.	8.
9.	10.	11.	12.
13.	14.	15.	16.
17.	18.	19.	20.

Lesson #9

1. What will the time be 7 minutes before noon?
2. 30,000 – 16,326 = ?
3. Is this figure a polygon?

4. Two figures having the same shape, but with different size are ____.
5. 835 ÷ 4 = ?
6. 6 × 7 = ?
7. Find the perimeter of the figure.

6 cm

3 cm

8. 137,662 + 151,294 = ?
9. How many inches are in 4 feet?
10. 32 × 26 = ?
11. How many degrees are in a straight angle?
12. 95 – ____ = 29
13. Five hundred years are ____________ centuries.
14. Draw a hexagon.
15. Which digit is in the hundred thousands place in 42,671,835?
16. How many quarters are in $5?
17. How many millimeters are in a meter?

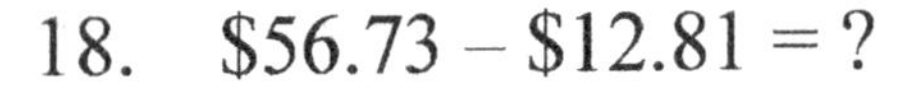

18. $56.73 – $12.81 = ?
19. Which is longer, 7 yards or 7 miles?
20. Mr. Thompson drove from Indianapolis to Milwaukee in 4 hours. If he drove 60 miles per hour, how many miles did he drive?

1.	2.	3.	4.
5.	6.	7.	8.
9.	10.	11.	12.
13.	14.	15.	16.
17.	18.	19.	20.

Lesson #10

1. Classify each angle below as acute, right, obtuse, or straight.

a.  b.  c. 

2. $1{,}206 \div 6 = ?$

3. Give the name of this shape.

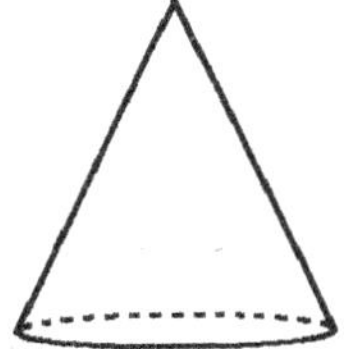

4. $3{,}005 - 1{,}265 = ?$

5. What is the average of 125, 115 and 108?

6. If the radius of a circle is 6 inches, what is the diameter?

7. Round 24,897,063 to the nearest million.

8. $50 \times 30 = ?$

9. What is the probability of the spinner landing on *A*?

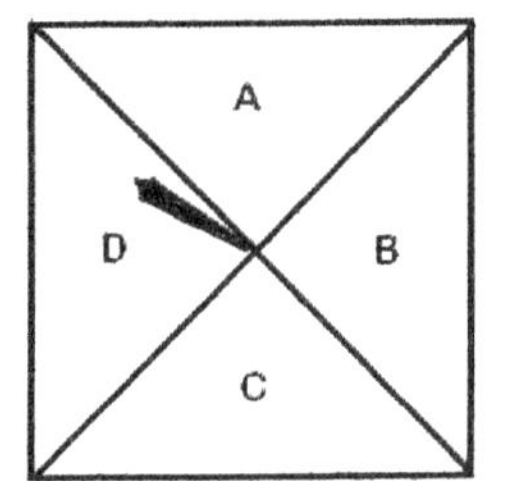

10. How many seconds are in 4 minutes?

11. On Saturday and Sunday a total of 614 people skated at the Rollercade. If the same number of people skated each day, how many people skated on Sunday?

12. Find the area of the square.

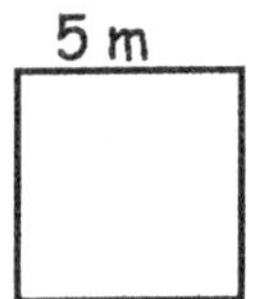

13. $13{,}805 \times 2 = ?$

14. Jeremy is 5 feet 4 inches tall. How many inches tall is Jeremy?

15. How many months are in 5 years?

16. Which digit is in the millions place in 56,870,513?

17. What fraction of the triangle is not shaded?

18. Which is longer, 6 feet or 6 yards?

19. Draw intersecting lines.

20. **The mode is the number that occurs most often in a set of numbers. The mode of 56, 78, 91, 22 and 78 is 78.** What is the mode of 23, 80, 45, 67 and 45?

1.	2.	3.	4.
5.	6.	7.	8.
9.	10.	11.	12.
13.	14.	15.	16.
17.	18.	19.	20.

Lesson #11

1. Find the mode of 18, 46, 21, 97, 18 and 33.
2. 40,133 + 25,615 = ?
3. The play began at 8:00 and lasted 90 minutes. At what time did the play end?
4. Draw a line segment.
5. 2,470 ÷ 53 = ?
6. How many inches are in a yard?
7. 125 × 24 = ?
8. Find the average of 22, 28 and 40.

9. Will a can of soda hold about 350 milliliters or 350 liters?
10. 4 × 8 = ?

11. The answer to an addition problem is called the ___________.
12. Round 4,576,089 to the nearest million.
13. What is the denominator in the fraction $\frac{8}{9}$?
14. 21,563 × 4 = ?
15. Draw a square. Draw a line of symmetry through the square.
16. Write the standard number for 80,000 + 6,000 + 400 + 90 + 2.
17. 500 – 234 = ?
18. Ted has $55. He wants to buy 3 magazines for $6 each and 3 CD's for $12 each. Does Ted have enough money to buy anything else? Explain how you got your answer.
19. Find the range of 62, 35, 10 and 76.
20. How many cookies are in 7 dozen?

1.	2.	3.	4.
5.	6.	7.	8.
9.	10.	11.	12.
13.	14.	15.	16.
17.	18.	19.	20.

Lesson #12

1. Any four-sided polygon is called a(n) ______________.

2. $86 \div 34 = ?$

3. Which is heavier, 9 grams or 9 kilograms?

4. $65 + 77 + 91 = ?$

5. Draw an acute angle.

6. $96 \times 34 = ?$

7. What is $\frac{1}{2}$ of 50?

8. Round 31,365,212 to the nearest ten thousand.

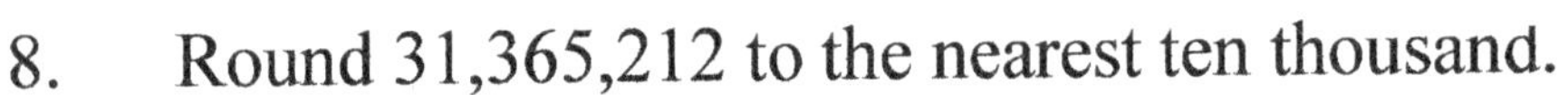

9. The answer in a division problem is called the ____________.

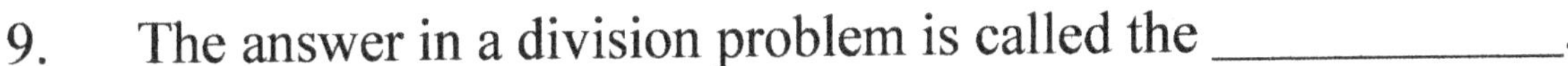

10. Find the mode of 79, 32, 17, 47, 32 and 87.

11. Which digit is in the ten millions place in 56,907,316?

12. **On the Fahrenheit temperature scale, water freezes at 32°F and it boils at 212°F.** Write *Fahrenheit freezing = 32°F* and *Fahrenheit boiling = 212°F.*

13. Name the type of angle.

14. Find the perimeter of this polygon.

47 mm
38 mm
32 mm
50 mm

15. $3{,}097 - 1{,}994 = ?$

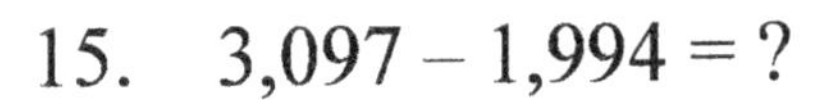

16. At 40 minutes before 5:00, what time is it?

17. How many degrees are in a straight angle?

18. There are __________ millimeters in a meter.

19. Find the average of 45, 47, 48 and 52.

20. Mr. Wilson needs to buy 4 tickets from Newark to San Francisco. What combination of tickets will cost $3,930?

Round Trip: Newark to San Francisco	
Ticket Class	Price
First Class	$1,500
Business	$975
Coach	$480

1.	2.	3.	4.
5.	6.	7.	8.
9.	10.	11.	12.
13.	14.	15.	16.
17.	18.	19.	20.

Lesson #13

1. What is the probability of getting a 7 on one roll of a die?

2. Round 46,709,231 to the nearest ten million.

3. What fraction is shaded?

4. 540 ÷ 60 = ?

5. How many teaspoons are in 8 tablespoons?

6. Find the area of the rectangle.

7. 671,154 + 255,607 = ?

8. Find the range of the numbers 45, 66, 21, 99 and 16.

9. Which digit is in the hundred millions place in 317,905,284?

10. Would a gasoline tank hold about 50 ml or 50 L of gasoline?

11. 12 × 55 = ?

12. Are these shapes congruent?

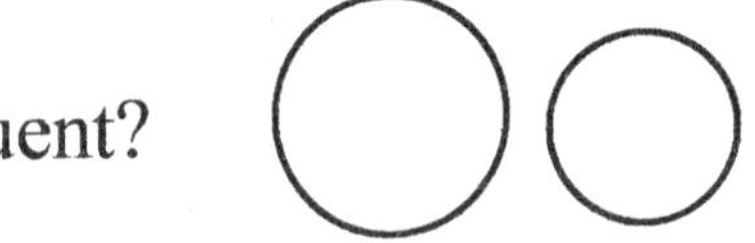

13. Draw a right angle.

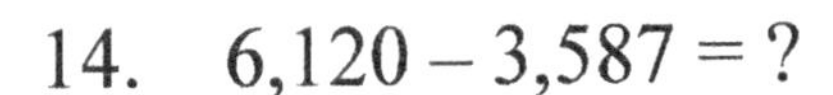

14. 6,120 – 3,587 = ?

15. On the Fahrenheit scale, water boils at _____.

16. How many decades are 60 years?

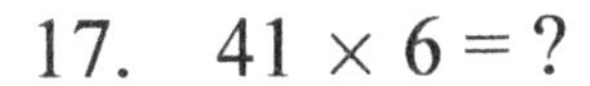

17. 41 × 6 = ?

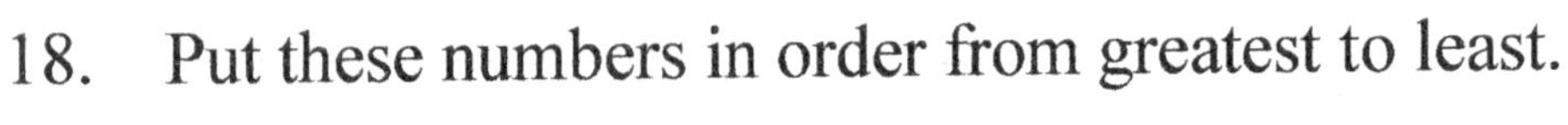

18. Put these numbers in order from greatest to least.

    4,896 4,901 4,899

19. 358 ÷ 4 = ?

20. Aaron works a total of 15 hours on Monday, Tuesday, and Wednesday. He works twice as many hours on Tuesday as he does on Monday. Aaron works 3 hours on Wednesday. How many hours does he work on Tuesday?

1.	2.	3.	4.
5.	6.	7.	8.
9.	10.	11.	12.
13.	14.	15.	16.
17.	18.	19.	20.

Lesson #14

1. Round 312,908,754 to the nearest ten million.
2. $46 \times 52 = ?$
3. How many centimeters are in 5 meters?
4. At 45 minutes after midnight, what will the time be?
5. Half of the diameter of a circle is called the __________
6. An apple would more likely weigh 200 grams or 200 kilograms?
7. Find the average of 52, 56 and 51.
8. $35 + 16 + 5 = ?$
9. Is this figure a polygon? 
10. $465 \div 25 = ?$
11. How many pints are in a quart?
12. On the Fahrenheit scale, water freezes at ________.
13. Find the perimeter of the trapezoid. 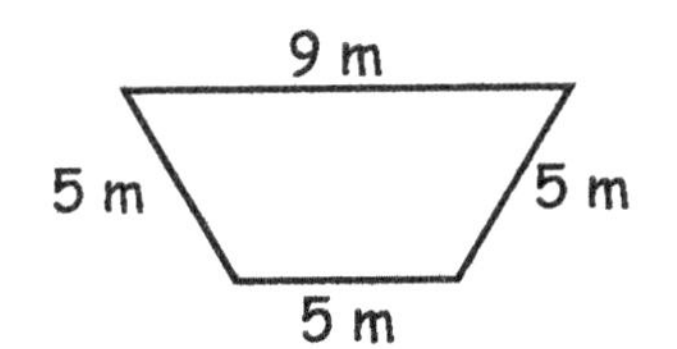

14. $43,180 - 17,461 = ?$
15. Joel is 6 feet 4 inches tall. What is Joel's height in inches?
16. Write the next number in the sequence. 122, 136, 150, …
17. The Girl Scouts made 840 bracelets in 5 hours. If they made the same number of bracelets each hour, how many did they make in one hour?
18. Any four-sided figure is called a(n) ____________.
19. Is the number 67,983 an even number or an odd number? How do you know?
20. What kind of angle measures less than 90°?

1.	2.	3.	4.
5.	6.	7.	8.
9.	10.	11.	12.
13.	14.	15.	16.
17.	18.	19.	20.

Lesson #15

1. How many degrees are in a straight angle?

2. 7,855 + 8,492 = ?

3. Would a cookie best be weighed in ounces or in pounds?

4. What is the probability of rolling a number greater than 3 on one roll of a die?

5. Are these shapes similar or congruent?

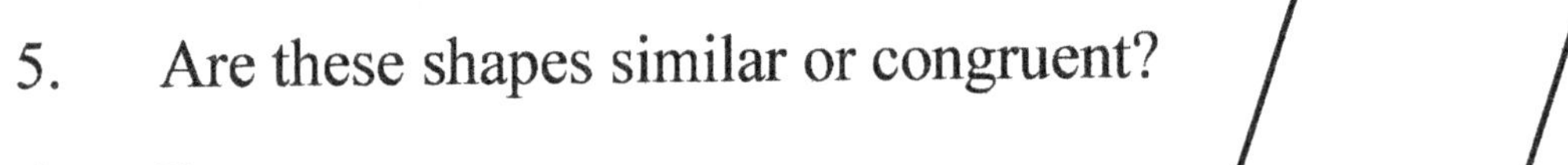

6. Draw a ray.

7. 62 × 32 = ?

8. Find the area.

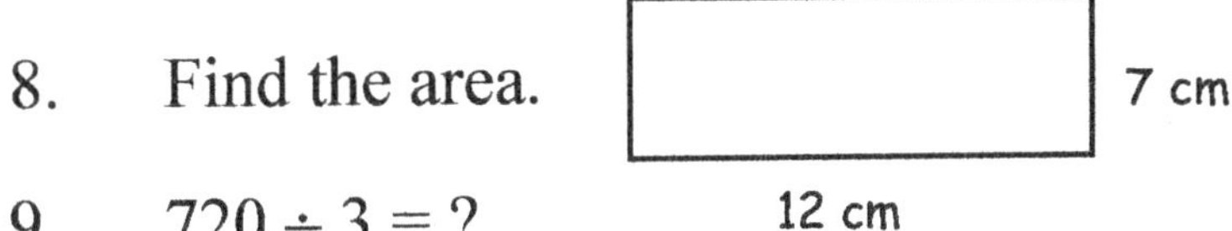

9. 720 ÷ 3 = ?

10. Seven quarters, 5 dimes, 3 nickels, and 4 pennies is how much money?

11. Find the range of 37, 76, 53 and 25.

12. Round 6,414,862 to the nearest thousand.

13. Water boils at what temperature on the Fahrenheit scale?

14. Is the figure a polygon?

15. 30,000 – 15,755 = ?

16. Write 27,384 in expanded form.

17. How many days are in 4 years?

18. If the radius of a circle is 14 meters, what is its diameter?

19. How many degrees are in a right angle?

20. Is the dotted line a line of symmetry in the arrow?

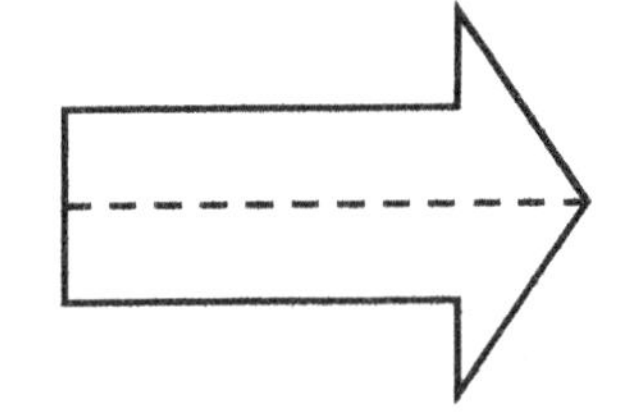

1.	2.	3.	4.
5.	6.	7.	8.
9.	10.	11.	12.
13.	14.	15.	16.
17.	18.	19.	20.

Lesson #16

1. $9{,}032 \div 4 = ?$

2. The answer to a subtraction problem is called the ______.

3. Which digit is in the hundred millions place in 468,097,132?

4. Find the median of 47, 18, 12, 30 and 20.

5. What are the first 4 prime numbers?

6. $40 \times 30 = ?$

7. How many millimeters are in a meter?

8. $502 - 236 = ?$

9. How many feet are in 3 miles?

10. It is 7:30. What time will it be in 10 hours?

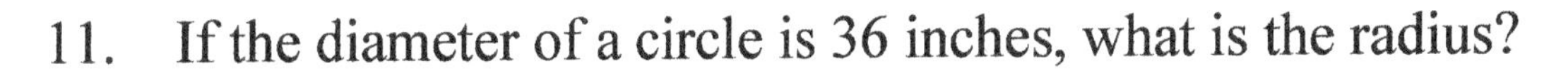

11. If the diameter of a circle is 36 inches, what is the radius?

12. Would a bike weigh 10 grams or 10 kilograms?

13. Draw 2 congruent circles.

14. The distance around the outside of a polygon is called the ________.

15. $66{,}013 + 28{,}727 = ?$

16. Find the average of 87, 91, 95, 92 and 85.

17. Round 78,493,211 to the nearest ten million.

Use the graph to answer questions 18 – 20.

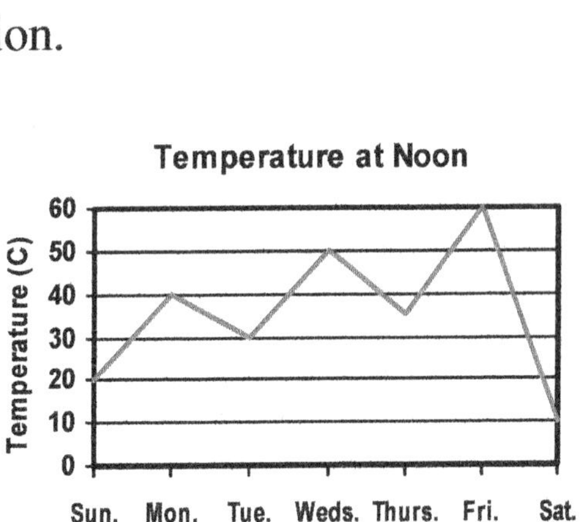

18. What is the average temperature for Monday, Tuesday, and Wednesday?

19. How much warmer was it on Wednesday than on Sunday?

20. Which day had the lowest temperature?

1.	2.	3.	4.
5.	6.	7.	8.
9.	10.	11.	12.
13.	14.	15.	16.
17.	18.	19.	20.

Lesson #17

1. Round 126,459,071 to the nearest hundred million.

2. What's the probability of rolling an even number on 1 roll of a die?

3. 45.6 + 19.2 = ?

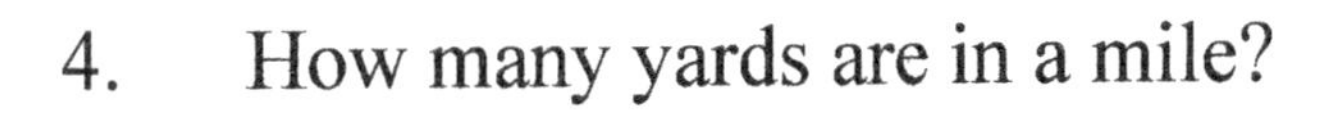

4. How many yards are in a mile?

5. 42,308 – 25,687 = ?

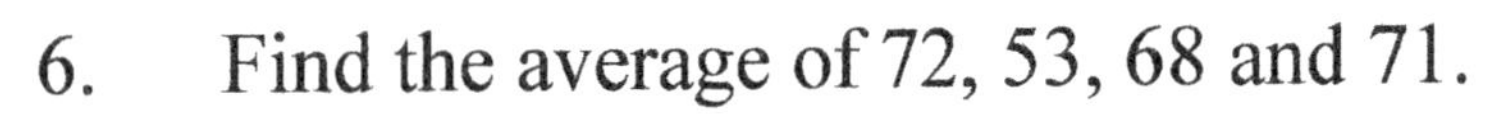

6. Find the average of 72, 53, 68 and 71.

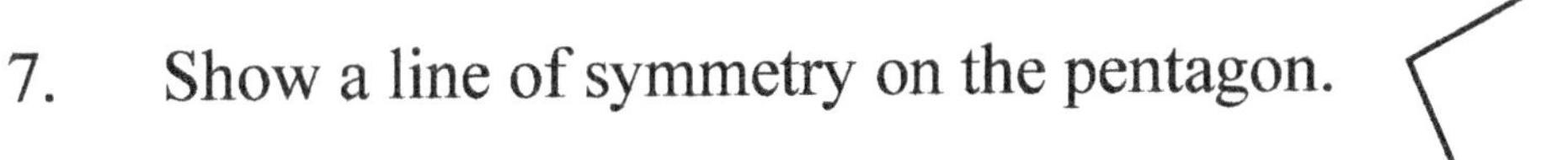

7. Show a line of symmetry on the pentagon.

8. 3,290 ÷ 7 = ?

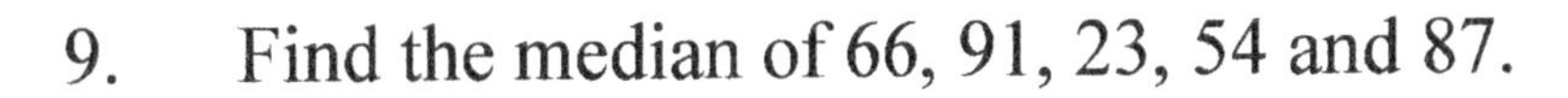

9. Find the median of 66, 91, 23, 54 and 87.

10. Find the perimeter of an octagon, if each side measures 5 inches.

11. Thirty students volunteered to set up booths for the school fair. All of the students worked 2 hours after school on Thursday and on Friday. Twelve of them also worked 3 hours on Wednesday. If they did this for 2 weeks, how many total hours were worked?

12. Two figures having the same shape, but different size are ________.

13. Identify the name of the shape.

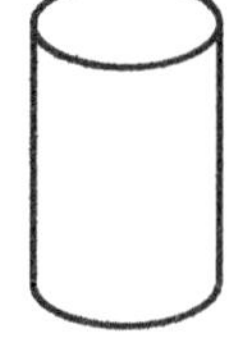

14. 47 × 52 = ?

15. 135 + 456 = ?

16. On the Fahrenheit scale, water freezes at ________.

17. Is the length of a screwdriver best measured in inches or in feet?

18. It is 2:25. What time will it be in 4 hours and 5 minutes?

19. The quotient is the answer to a(n) ________ problem.

20. Write the formula for finding the area of a rectangle.

1.	2.	3.	4.
5.	6.	7.	8.
9.	10.	11.	12.
13.	14.	15.	16.
17.	18.	19.	20.

Lesson #18

1. 67,642 + 22,518 = ?
2. How many millimeters are in 3 meters?
3. Which digit is in the ten millions place in 46,098,125?
4. 9 × 7 = ?
5. How many feet are in 3 yards?

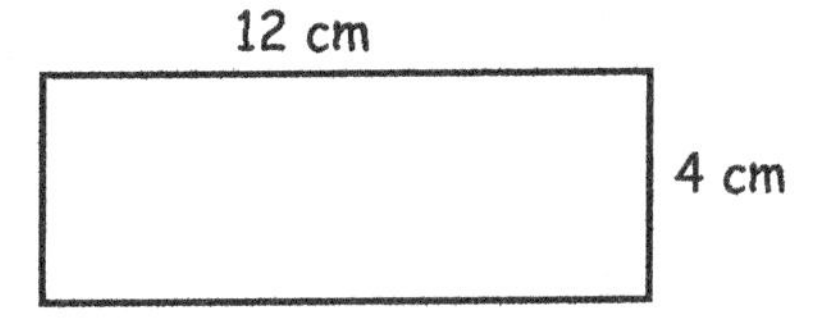

6. What is the area of the rectangle?
7. Find the range of 75, 15, 33, 96 and 14.
8. Draw perpendicular lines.
9. 23.9 + 45.6 = ?
10. How many degrees are in a straight angle?
11. 122 × 31 = ?
12. Write the time shown on the clock.
13. 4,685 ÷ 5 = ?
14. A pentagon has __________ sides.

15. The distance that is half of the diameter is called the ________.
16. 50,000 – 16,332 = ?

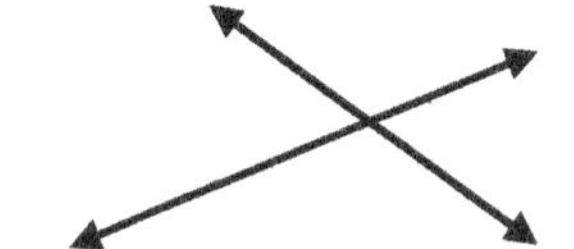

17. Identify the type of lines.
18. Write the next number in the sequence. 75, 90, 105, …
19. Write the standard number for
    1,000,000 + 400,000 + 30,000 + 3,000 + 500.
20. A social studies teacher received 25 reports on The Civil War from her class. Each report was 15 pages long. What is the total number of pages the teacher will have to read?

1.	2.	3.	4.
5.	6.	7.	8.
9.	10.	11.	12.
13.	14.	15.	16.
17.	18.	19.	20.

Lesson #19

1. 3,000 – 1,599 = ?

2. 65 × 22 = ?

3. Draw a line of symmetry through the arrow.

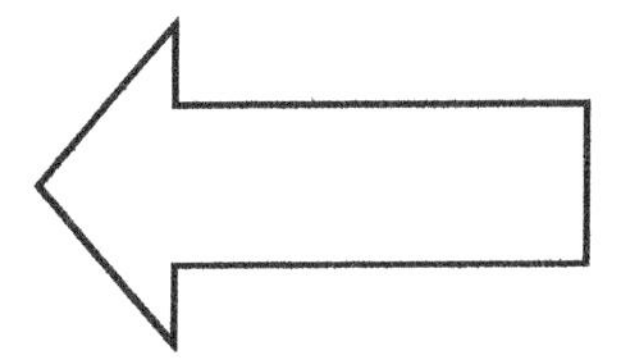

4. On the Fahrenheit scale, water boils at _____.

5. Which digit is in the hundred millions place in 309,652,784?

6. 987 ÷ 47 = ?

7. Find the median of 62, 30, 28, 91 and 13.

8. 21,809 × 4 = ?

9. 82,730 + 35,896 = ?

10. Round 47,292,561 to the nearest million.

11. 125.98 + 211.54 = ?

12. How many cups are in 3 pints?

13. Write the next number in the sequence. 355, 376, 397, …

14. How many quarters are in $2.25?

15. How many ounces are in 6 pounds?

16. What is the warmest time of day? How many degrees did the temperature rise between 8:00 a.m. and 2:00 p.m.?

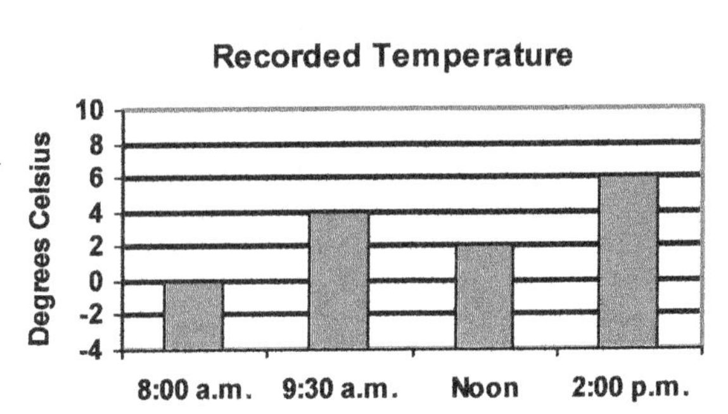

17. 63 ÷ 9 = ?

18. Natasha made 35 bracelets. She usually sells them for $10 each. If she sells 20 bracelets at the regular price and sells the remaining 15 bracelets for half price, how much money will Natasha make?

19. Barry is 4 feet 7 inches tall. What is Barry's height in inches?

20. 56,893 ◯ 56,398

1.	2.	3.	4.
5.	6.	7.	8.
9.	10.	11.	12.
13.	14.	15.	16.
17.	18.	19.	20.

Lesson #20

1. If the radius of a circle is 16 cm, what is its diameter?
2. 569,832 + 56,354 = ?
3. Give the probability of rolling a number less than 5 on one roll of a die?
4. Find the area of the quadrilateral.

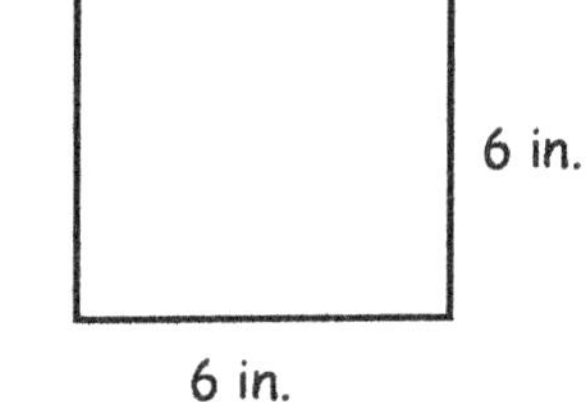

5. Draw a line segment.
6. $31 \times 27 = ?$
7. 6,000 – 3,631 = ?
8. What is the numerator in the fraction $\frac{3}{8}$?
9. Which digit is in the hundred millions place in 895,367,402?
10. If it is 7:35 now, what time was it 4 hours and 15 minutes ago?
11. Joey's math scores for this quarter are 79, 82, 93, 91 and 100. What is Joey's average score?
12. List the first five even numbers.
13. An eight-sided polygon is called a(n) __________.
14. How many feet are in 2 miles?
15. $5{,}760 \div 8 = ?$
16. Are these figures similar?

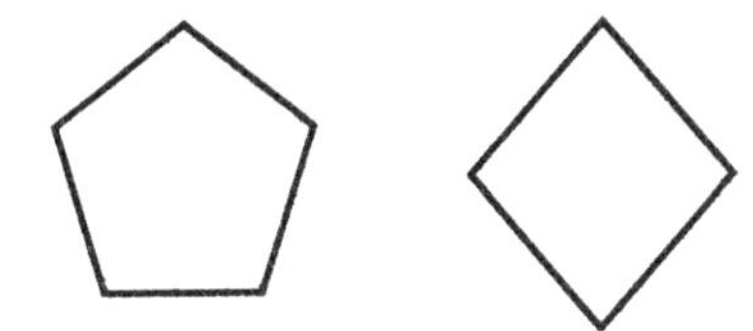

17. $835 \times 3 = ?$
18. What do you call the number that is left over after one number is divided into another number?
19. How many weeks are 63 days?
20. The answer to a subtraction problem is called the ______________.

1.	2.	3.	4.
5.	6.	7.	8.
9.	10.	11.	12.
13.	14.	15.	16.
17.	18.	19.	20.

Lesson #21

1. Which digit is in the ten millions place in 40,571,236?

2. 12,356 ÷ 4 = ?

3. Draw intersecting lines.

4. A right angle measures ________ degrees.

5. How many years are 5 centuries?

6. 84 × 43 = ?

7. Find the area.

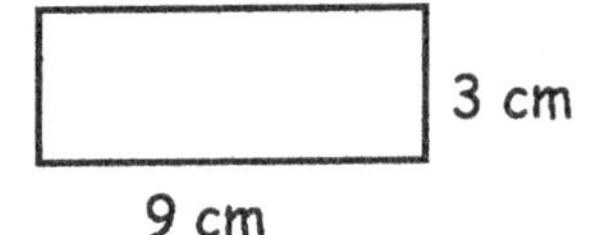

8. 56 + 31 + 18 = ?

9. How many pints are in a quart?

10. **A prime number is a number greater than 1 with exactly two different factors: 1 and the number itself.** Some examples of prime numbers are: 2, 3, 5, 11, 23 and 91. Is 13 a prime number?

11. Write the missing number in this sequence. 25, 40, ____, 70, 85

12. The answer to a multiplication problem is called the ________.

13. List the even numbers between 80 and 91.

14. 4.6 – 1.7 = ?

15. What is the time 10 minutes before noon?

16. Round 27,887,530 to the nearest hundred thousand.

17. 78.2 + 34.9 = ?

18. Identify the type of angle.

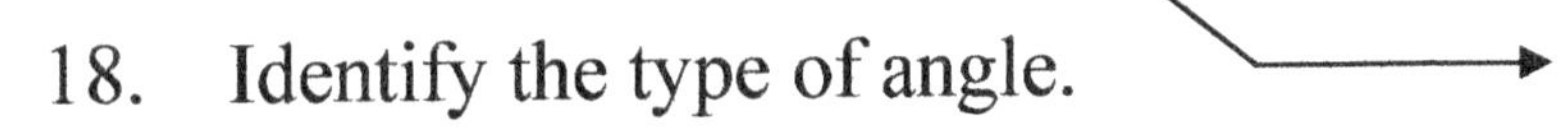

19. How much further had the Plover traveled than the Bobolink after 3 hours?

20. What is the difference in the total miles traveled after 4 hours?

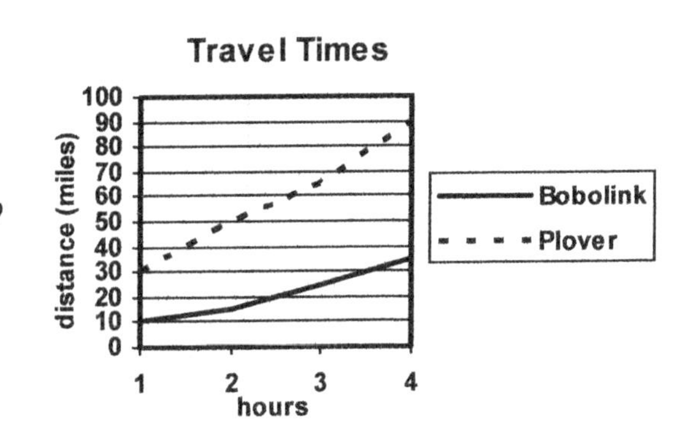

1.	2.	3.	4.
5.	6.	7.	8.
9.	10.	11.	12.
13.	14.	15.	16.
17.	18.	19.	20.

Lesson #22

1. How many millimeters are in 5 meters?
2. 47 + ____ = 81
3. Draw a ray.
4. If a baby squirrel weighs 96 ounces. What is the squirrel's weight in pounds?

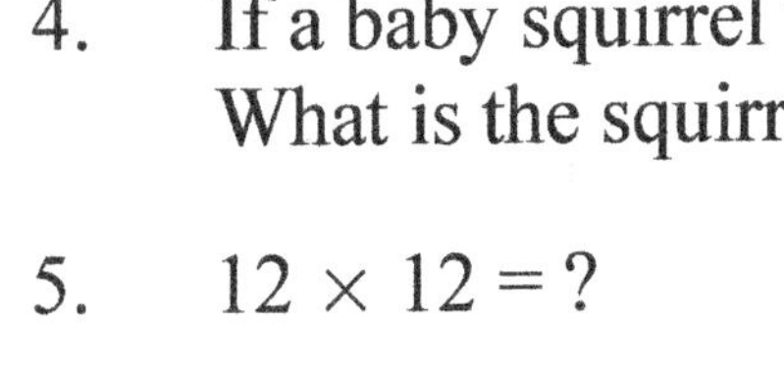

5. $12 \times 12 = ?$
6. Which digit is in the millions place in the number 23,870,194?
7. **On the Celsius scale, water freezes at 0°C and boils at 100°C.** Write *Celsius freezing = 0°C* and *Celsius boiling = 100°C.*
8. $34 \times 42 = ?$
9. Liquid in an eyedropper is best measured in milliliters or in liters?
10. Round 683,265,721 to the nearest ten million.
11. $567 \div 63 = ?$
12. Write the name of this shape.

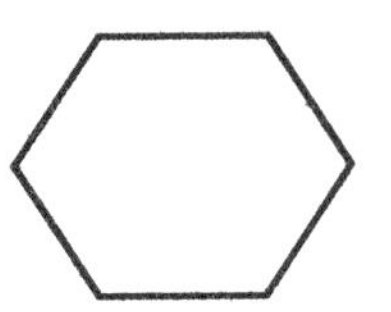

13. $32 \div 8 = ?$
14. If it is 6:55 now, what time was it 3 hours and 25 minutes ago?
15. What fraction is shaded?

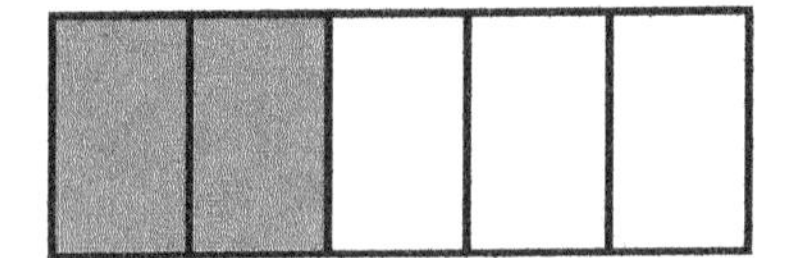

16. $6{,}219 - 3{,}988 = ?$
17. How many feet are in 5 yards?
18. Half of a circle's diameter is called its __________.
19. What do you call the top number in a fraction?
20. Tom and Karen are traveling to Italy. They want to take at least 300 pictures of the country. If each roll of film contains 24 pictures, will 12 rolls of film be enough? Explain your answer.

1.	2.	3.	4.
5.	6.	7.	8.
9.	10.	11.	12.
13.	14.	15.	16.
17.	18.	19.	20.

Lesson #23

1. $32{,}876 \div 4 = ?$

2. An eight-sided polygon is called a(n) __________.

3. Draw intersecting lines.

4. Find the perimeter of the square. 6 ft

5. $47 \times 22 = ?$

6. On the Celsius scale, water freezes at ______.

7. Are these shapes similar or congruent?

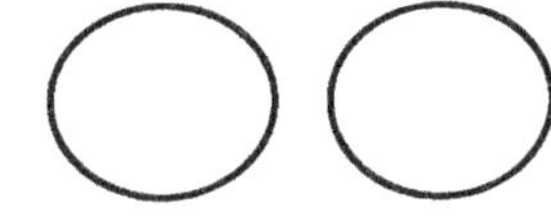

8. $70{,}000 - 57{,}349 = ?$

9. Which digit is in the millions place in 96,045,812?

10. Round 8,927,014 to the nearest hundred thousand.

11. $157.92 + 68.5 = ?$

12. Write the name of this shape.

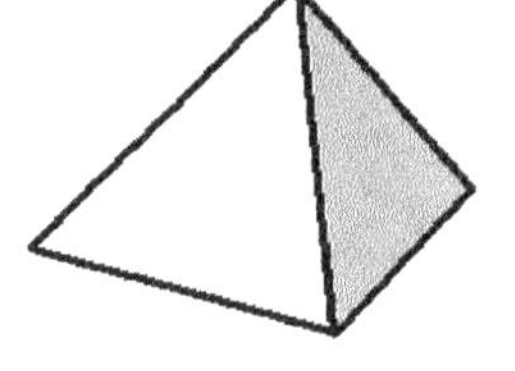

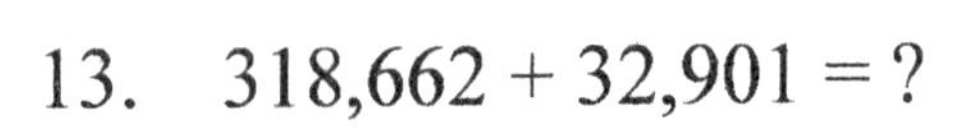

13. $318{,}662 + 32{,}901 = ?$

14. Find the median of 75, 15, 29, 41 and 60.

15. Which is longer, a meter or a kilometer?

16. List the factors of 18.

17. A plane weighs 4 tons. How many pounds does it weigh?

18. **A composite number is a number that has more than 2 factors.** An example of a composite number is 24. Twenty-four has 8 factors (1, 2, 3, 4, 6, 8, 12 and 24). Is 18 a prime or a composite number?

19. Write the first four prime numbers.

20. Rickie has 648 baseball cards. He wants to put them into an album. If each page of the album holds 12 cards, how many pages are needed to hold all of his cards?

1.	2.	3.	4.
5.	6.	7.	8.
9.	10.	11.	12.
13.	14.	15.	16.
17.	18.	19.	20.

Lesson #24

1. Is the number 17 prime or composite?
2. How many teaspoons are in 9 tablespoons?
3. List the factors of 20.
4. What is the probability that the spinner will land on a vowel? On the letter F?

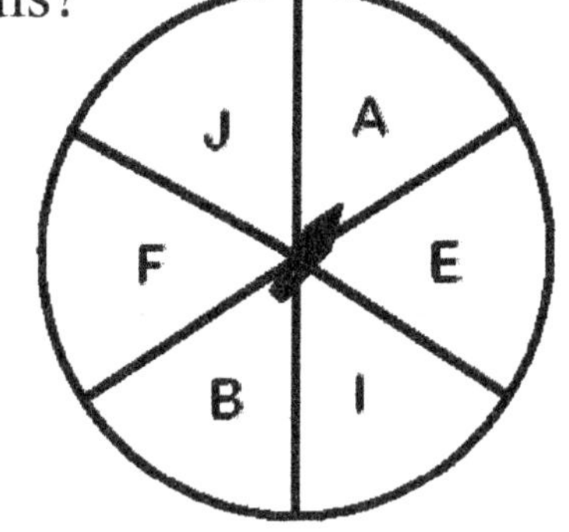

5. 7.35 + 13.8 = ?
6. Round 46,798,320 to the nearest hundred thousand.
7. Write 273,542 in expanded form.

8. $6 \times 5 \times 3 = ?$
9. Draw a line of symmetry.

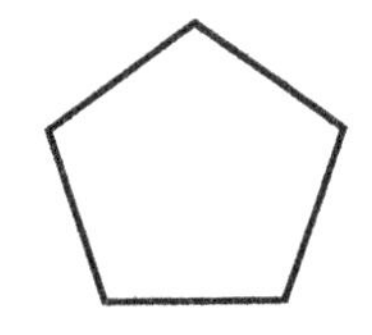

10. $55 \times 35 = ?$
11. Find the average of 310, 421 and 424.
12. On the Celsius scale, water boils at ________.
13. How many yards are in 3 miles?
14. 5,106 – 2,364 = ?
15. Gerald is 5 feet 5 inches tall. What is Gerald's height in inches?
16. 5,508 ÷ 54 = ?
17. Draw parallel horizontal lines.
18. Find the mode of 40, 76, 99, 10 and 76.
19. The wedding reception began at 7:30. Everyone went home at 11:00. How long was the reception?
20. 19.6 – 12.8 = ?

1.	2.	3.	4.
5.	6.	7.	8.
9.	10.	11.	12.
13.	14.	15.	16.
17.	18.	19.	20.

Lesson #25

1. Draw a hexagon.

2. 56,304 + 27,138 = ?

3. Would the length of a car be about 4 meters or 4 kilometers?

4. List the factors of 25.

5. A number that has only 2 factors is called a __________ number.

6. **Prime factoring is writing a number as a product its prime factors.** *See the Help Pages for examples.* Make a factor tree for 24. Write the answer as a product of prime numbers. Use exponents if needed.

7. 503 – 175 = ?

8. Find the area.

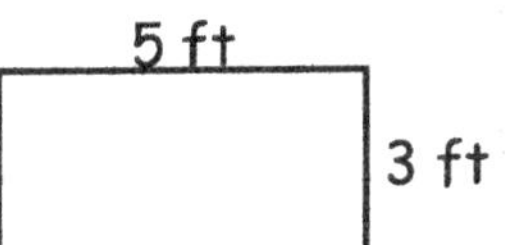

9. 12,351 × 6 = ?

10. Round 4,809,467 to the nearest million.

11. 93.44 – 36.28 = ?

12. How many meters are in 700 centimeters?

13. 156,972 ◯ 155,803

14. 21,345 ÷ 3 = ?

15. Is 36 a prime number or a composite number?

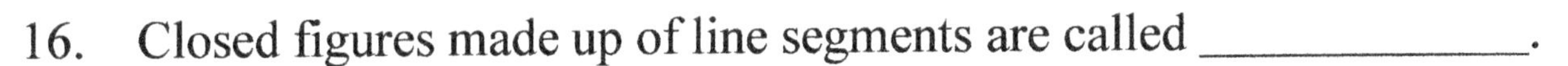

16. Closed figures made up of line segments are called ______________.

17. Give the Celsius and Fahrenheit freezing temperatures of water.

18. What is the denominator in the fraction $\frac{9}{10}$?

19. Lauren plays the piano on Tuesdays, Wednesdays, and Thursdays for 30 minutes. She plays for 50 minutes on Saturdays, Sundays, and Mondays. How many hours does Lauren play piano each week?

20. How many grams are in 5 kilograms?

1.	2.	3.	4.
5.	6.	7.	8.
9.	10.	11.	12.
13.	14.	15.	16.
17.	18.	19.	20.

Lesson #26

1. $16{,}464 \div 4 = ?$

2. Make a factor tree for 45. Write the factors in order from least to greatest using exponents when needed.

3. Find the area of the rectangle.

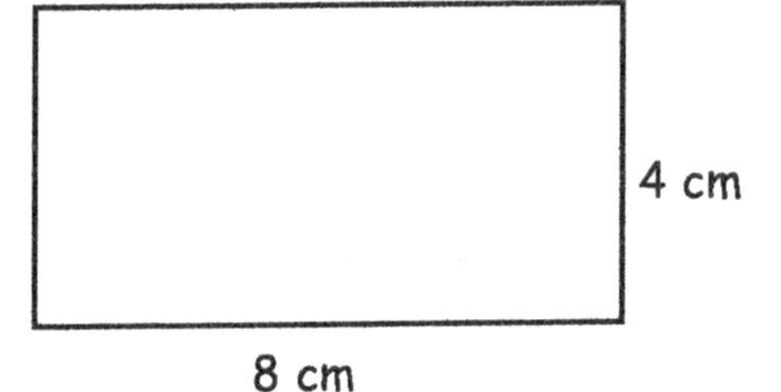

4. $51 \times 32 = ?$

5. $9{,}339 + 8{,}752 = ?$

6. Would a dog weigh about 15 ounces or 15 pounds?

7. It is 2:30 pm. How much time has passed since noon?

8. Is 29 a prime or a composite number?

9. The prime factorization of a number is $2 \times 3 \times 7$. What is the number?

10. Which digit is in the thousands place in 21,086,347?

11. There are 338 students and teachers going on a field trip to the zoo. Each bus holds 42 people. How many buses are needed for the trip?

12. $39.41 + 16.7 = ?$

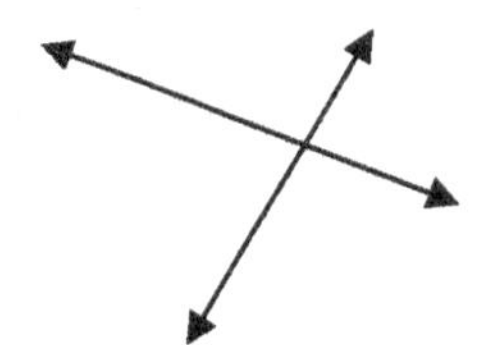

13. Are these lines perpendicular?

14. List the factors of 12.

15. The answer to a multiplication problem is called the ____________.

16. Is 67,893 an even number or an odd number?

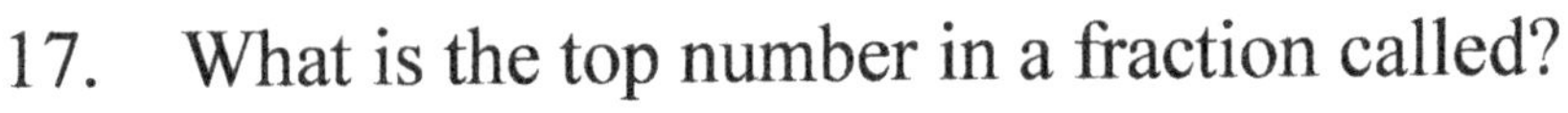

17. What is the top number in a fraction called?

18. Draw an acute angle.

19. $30{,}000 - 12{,}335 = ?$

20. How many cups are in 4 pints?

1.	2.	3.	4.
5.	6.	7.	8.
9.	10.	11.	12.
13.	14.	15.	16.
17.	18.	19.	20.

Lesson #27

1. Find the perimeter of the rectangle.

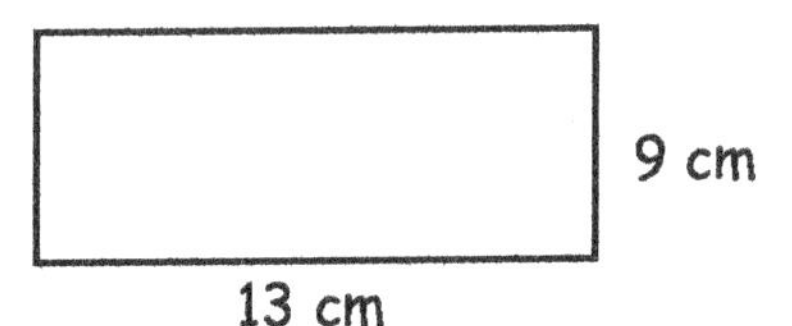

2. $3{,}435 \times 3 = ?$
3. Draw an obtuse angle.
4. Find the mode in 17, 25, 53, 17 and 69.
5. Gina loves to read mysteries. She read 10 books the first week, 11 books the second week and 15 books during the third week. Find the average number of mystery books Gina reads weekly.
6. Make a factor tree for 35.

7. $145{,}214 + 68{,}382 = ?$
8. How many quarts are in 6 gallons?
9. $20{,}000 - 16{,}832 = ?$
10. List the factors of 18.

11. If a bus weighs 7 tons. What is its weight in pounds?

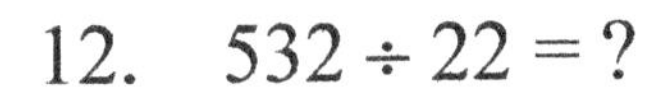

12. $532 \div 22 = ?$
13. Are these shapes congruent or similar?

14. $156.33 - 78.15 = ?$
15. Which digit is in the hundred millions place in 402,938,165?
16. How many ounces are in 3 pounds?
17. At what temperature does water boil on the Fahrenheit scale?
18. The prime factorization of a number is $2^3 \times 3^2$. What is the number?
19. What is the difference between the populations of the largest city and the smallest city?
20. What is the <u>estimated</u> total population of these four towns? Round to the nearest ten thousand.

Town	Population
Jefferson	23,851
Lincolnton	89,403
Franklin	53,925
Valley View	42,366

1.	2.	3.	4.
5.	6.	7.	8.
9.	10.	11.	12.
13.	14.	15.	16.
17.	18.	19.	20.

Lesson #28

1. The distance across the center of a circle is called the __________.
2. What is the average of these numbers? 1,121 1,087 1,095
3. Make a factor tree for the number 64.
4. Draw perpendicular lines.
5. Find the perimeter of the triangle.

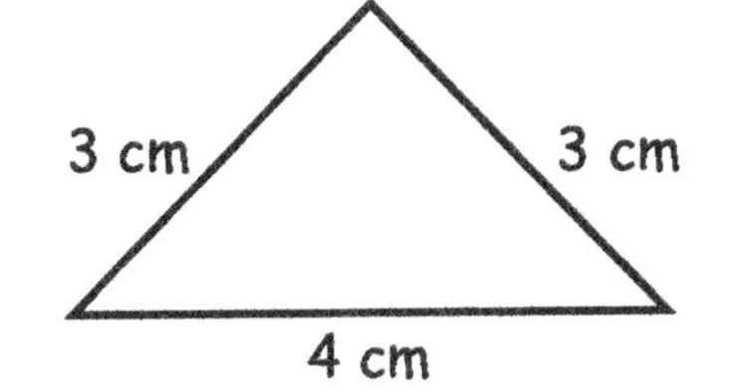

6. 38,513 – 16,579 = ?
7. Choose the sensible length of a key: 5 centimeters or 5 meters.
8. 491 + 77 = ?
9. What is the probability of landing on an odd number? On a number greater than 1?

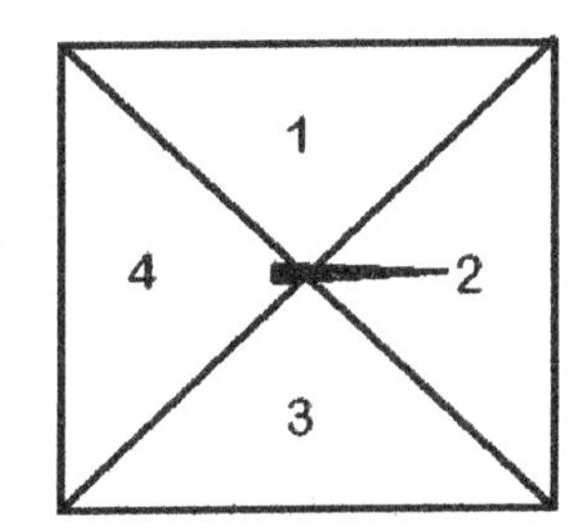

10. 4,604 ◯ 4,406
11. Is the number 45 a prime or a composite number?
12. Round 32,415,266 to the nearest thousand.
13. Make a factor tree for 36.
14.  $4 \times 29 = ?$
15.  $2{,}745 \div 5 = ?$

16. Which digit is in the millions place in 13,576,249?
17.  $24 \times 62 = ?$
18. Identify the type of angle.
19. 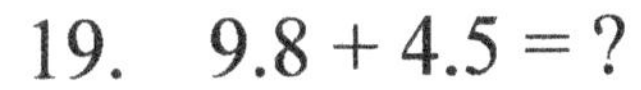 $9.8 + 4.5 = ?$
20. During the work week, Mrs. Jamison drives 75 miles each way to work. If she works 21 days each month, how far does she drive for work during the month?

1.	2.	3.	4.
5.	6.	7.	8.
9.	10.	11.	12.
13.	14.	15.	16.
17.	18.	19.	20.

Lesson #29

1. If the radius of a circle is 16 cm, what is its diameter?

2. Find the average of 87, 85 and 98.

3. 912 ÷ 3 = ?

4. 200 × 800 = ?

5. What do you call a number that has more than 2 factors?

6. List the factors of 21.

7. **Volume is a measure of space inside of a solid figure. The volume of a rectangular prism is the product of its length, width, and height. (L × W × H)** Find the volume of this figure.

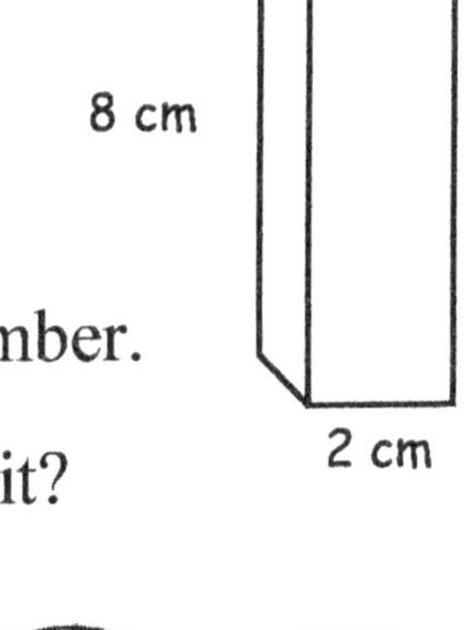

8. 7,000 – 2,336 = ?

9. Draw a ray.

10. 236,891 + 452,972 = ?

11. Write 50,000 + 9,000 + 300 + 60 + 2 as a standard number.

12. If it is 2 hours and 20 minutes after 7:00, what time is it?

13. Is 67 a prime number or composite number?

14. Make a factor tree for 24.

15. How many weeks are in 9 months?

16. 675 ÷ 25 = ?

17. A four-sided polygon is called a(n) ____________.

18. How many yards are in a mile?

19. Write the first 3 prime numbers.

20. The Youth Football team is selling candy to raise money for new uniforms. They earn $2 on each box of candy. If the uniforms cost $376, how many boxes of candy will the football team need to sell?

1.	2.	3.	4.
5.	6.	7.	8.
9.	10.	11.	12.
13.	14.	15.	16.
17.	18.	19.	20.

Lesson #30

1. Round 680,312,457 to the nearest ten million.

2. List the Celsius and Fahrenheit boiling temperatures of water.

3. Find the mode of 63, 52, 88, 63 and 37.

4. $63 \times 35 = ?$

5. How many inches are in 4 feet?

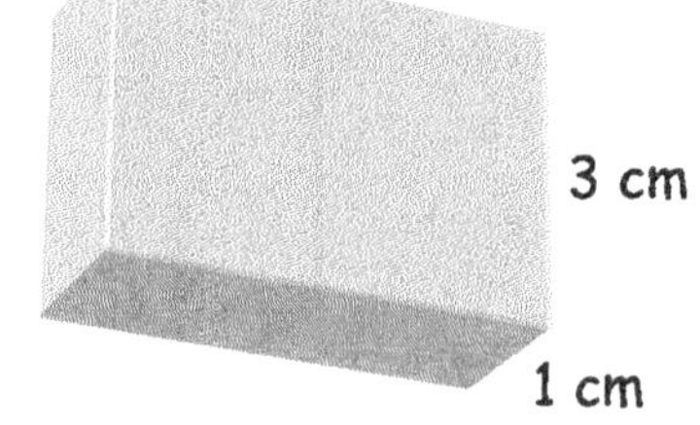

6. $800{,}000 - 581{,}365 = ?$

7. Find the volume of this rectangular prism.

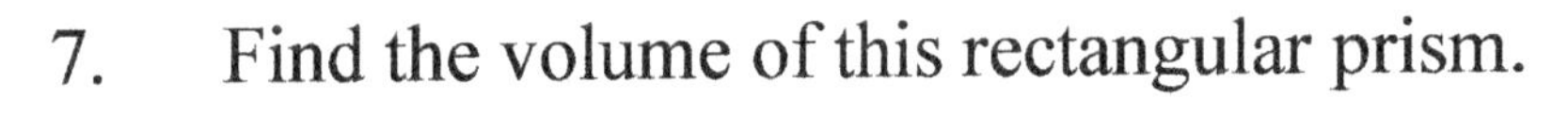

8. Make a factor tree for 48.

9. How many teaspoons are in 9 tablespoons?

10. It is 3:25. What time will it be in 5 hours and 5 minutes?

11. $3{,}836 \div 36 = ?$

12. What is the perimeter of the square?

13. $36.8 - 19.9 = ?$

14. An angle that measures more than 90° is called ___________.

15. Brian wants to buy a new bicycle that costs $195. He works after school for 12 hours a week and earns $5 per hour. How many weeks will it take Brian to earn enough money to buy the bicycle?

16. $864 + 399 = ?$

17. How many pints are in 6 quarts?

18. Which is longer, 10 yards or 10 feet?

19. Find the range of 100, 89, 74 and 32.

20. List the factors of 16.

1.	2.	3.	4.
5.	6.	7.	8.
9.	10.	11.	12.
13.	14.	15.	16.
17.	18.	19.	20.

Lesson #31

1. Fran has 250 red beads. She has twice as many blue beads as red beads. Fran has half as many yellow beads as red beads. How many beads does Fran have?

2. 288,654 + 176,349 = ?

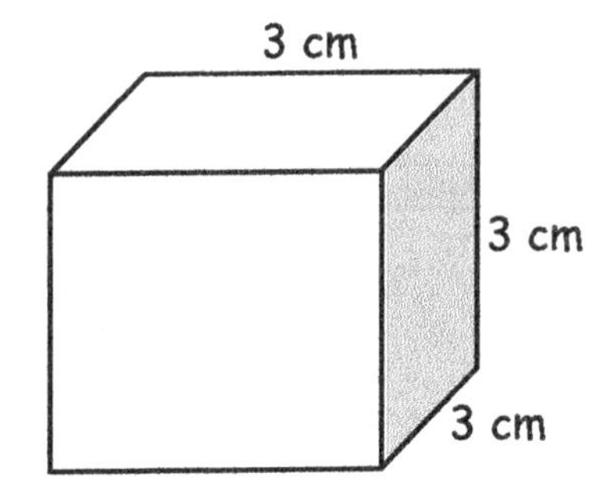

3. Draw a line segment.

4. Find the volume of the cube.

5. $50 \times 28 = ?$

6. Is the number 36 prime or composite?

7. $8.3 - 5.7 = ?$

8. 43 + ____ = 79

9. Make a factor tree for 40.

10. $8{,}054 \times 5 = ?$

11. It is 1:05. What time was it 3 hours ago?

12. On the Celsius scale, water freezes at ______.

13. How many minutes are in 3 hours?

14. List the factors of 15.

15. $8{,}346 \div 6 = ?$

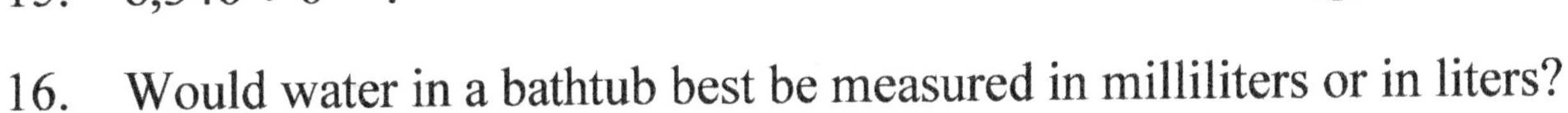

16. Would water in a bathtub best be measured in milliliters or in liters?

17. Draw perpendicular lines.

18. What is the bottom number in a fraction called?

19. Write the odd numbers between 60 and 68.

20. What is the probability of getting heads on one flip of a coin?

1.	2.	3.	4.
5.	6.	7.	8.
9.	10.	11.	12.
13.	14.	15.	16.
17.	18.	19.	20.

Lesson #32

1. Any four-sided polygon is called a(n) ______________.

2. Forty years are __________ decades.

3. Make a factor tree for 54.

4. Round 25,397,165 to the nearest ten million.

5. List the factors of 24. (There are 8 factors.)

6. $36 \times 71 = ?$

7. $52.3 + 29.9 = ?$

8. Find the volume of the prism.

5 ft
2 ft
2 ft

9. $134{,}268 + 642{,}338 = ?$

10. Closed figures made up of line segments are called ________.

11. Find the mode of 81, 55, 37, 48 and 55.

12. Draw a straight angle. How many degrees are in a straight angle?

13. $50{,}000 - 29{,}215 = ?$

14. The answer to a division problem is the ______________.

15. How many inches are in 5 feet?

16. **The Greatest Common Factor (GCF) of two or more numbers is the common factor that is greater than the others.** *See the Help Pages for examples.* Find the GCF of 12 and 15.

17. Is the number 44 a prime or a composite number?

18. $7{,}256 \div 3 = ?$

19. Bonnie read 17 pages on Monday, 22 pages on Tuesday, 13 pages on Wednesday, and 16 pages on Thursday. What is the average number of pages Bonnie read each day?

20. $12 \times 12 = ?$

1.	2.	3.	4.
5.	6.	7.	8.
9.	10.	11.	12.
13.	14.	15.	16.
17.	18.	19.	20.

Lesson #33

1. Find the GCF of 12 and 15.
2. $72 \times 43 = ?$
3. Write the first 5 prime numbers.
4. Make a factor tree for 56.
5. How many degrees are in a right angle?
6. List the factors of 20.
7. $235{,}679 + 375{,}886 = ?$
8. Find the average of 81, 78, 82 and 91.
9. $42{,}740 \div 5 = ?$

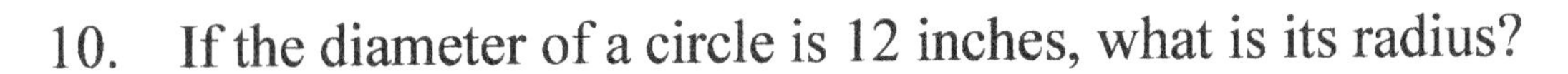

10. If the diameter of a circle is 12 inches, what is its radius?
11. $602 - 288 = ?$

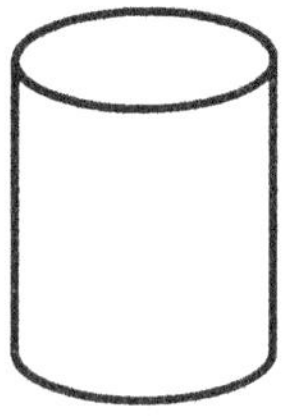

12. What is the name of this shape?

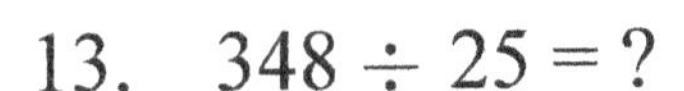

13. $348 \div 25 = ?$
14. How many weeks are the same as 140 days?
15. Round 85,765,023 to the nearest million.
16. Twice a week, Mario works a 6-hour day for $6.00 per hour. Three days a week, he works an 8-hour a day for $7.00 per hour. How much does he earn each week?
17. An angle that measures less than 90° is called _____________.
18. Find the area of a square whose sides measure 12 inches each.
19. Find the median of 25, 39, 96, 53 and 21.
20. Write the formula for finding the volume of a rectangular solid.

1.	2.	3.	4.
5.	6.	7.	8.
9.	10.	11.	12.
13.	14.	15.	16.
17.	18.	19.	20.

Lesson #34

1. Make a factor tree for 81.

2. **The Least Common Multiple (LCM) of two or more numbers is the smallest multiple they have in common.** *See the Help Pages for examples.* Find the LCM of 8 and 12.

3. Write the even numbers between 41 and 47.

4. What number is in the numerator in the fraction $\frac{6}{7}$?

5. 82,345 – 66,592 = ?

6. The distance across a circle, through the center, is the ___________.

7. Charlie had football practice after school. If practice started at 3:30 and lasted 1 hour and 30 minutes, what time was it over?

8. How many feet are in 5 miles?

9. Find the Greatest Common Factor (GCF) of 15 and 35.

10. A eight-sided polygon is called a(n) _______________.

11. On the Fahrenheit scale, water freezes at ___________.

12. Which digit is in the hundred millions place in 946,870,132?

13. How many cups are in 4 pints?

14. Find the volume of the prism to the right.

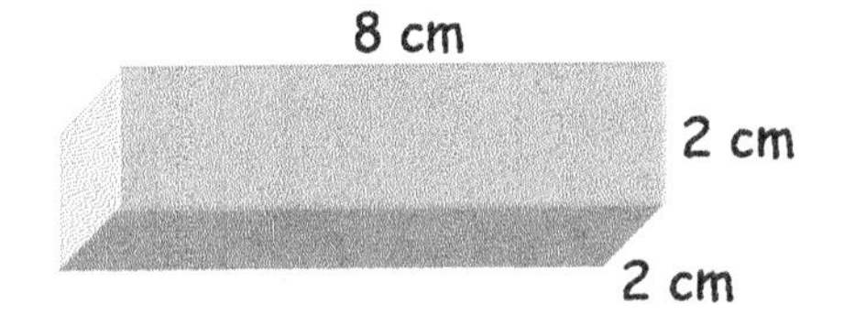

15. List the factors of 14.

16. $685 \div 25 = ?$

17. $64 + 19 + 33 = ?$

18. Find the range of 109, 132, 117, 150 and 179.

19. $22{,}908 \times 3 = ?$

20. Draw 2 similar squares.

1.	2.	3.	4.
5.	6.	7.	8.
9.	10.	11.	12.
13.	14.	15.	16.
17.	18.	19.	20.

Lesson #35

1. Draw a heart. Show a line of symmetry on the heart.
2. Is the number 43 prime or composite?
3. How many centimeters are in 7 meters?
4. $73 \times 35 = ?$
5. List the factors of 12.
6. If it is 6:45 now, what time was it 5 hours and 15 minutes ago?
7. What is the probability of rolling an odd number on 1 roll of a die?
8. The answer to a multiplication problem is the ____________.
9. Draw perpendicular lines.
10. $7.6 + 4.8 = ?$
11. $3{,}078 \div 4 = ?$
12. Make a factor tree for 32.
13. How many quarters are in $6.00?
14. How many feet are in 6 yards?
15. $40{,}000 - 28{,}356 = ?$

16. Write 80,000 + 6,000 + 30 + 5 as a standard number.
17. How many months are there from November 1st to April 1st?
18. Jackie's score on her social studies test was 6 points higher than Mark's score. Shauna's score was 10 points lower than Jackie's score. William's score was 4 points higher than Shauna's score. Mark scored a 90 on his test. What was each student's test score? Explain your thinking.
19. Find the Least Common Multiple of 12 and 18.
20. List the factors of 25.

1.	2.	3.	4.
5.	6.	7.	8.
9.	10.	11.	12.
13.	14.	15.	16.
17.	18.	19.	20.

Lesson #36

1. Find the LCM of 10 and 18.

2. $36{,}720 \div 5 = ?$

3. Is the number 48 prime or composite?

4. Put the fraction $\frac{5}{10}$ in simplest form.

5. $16{,}421 \times 5 = ?$

6. Draw a vertical line.

7. A(n) ______________ has six sides.

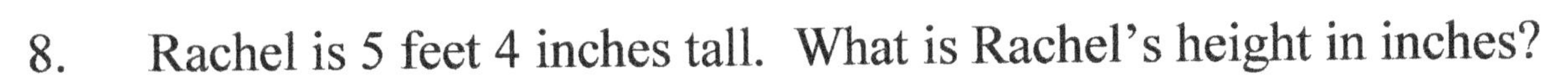

8. Rachel is 5 feet 4 inches tall. What is Rachel's height in inches?

9. How many degrees are in a straight angle?

10. Round 3,254,687 to the nearest thousand.

11. A jet weighs 7 tons. How many pounds does it weigh?

12. Find the GCF of 12 and 18.

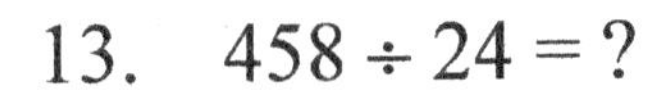

13. $458 \div 24 = ?$

14. Find the volume of the prism.

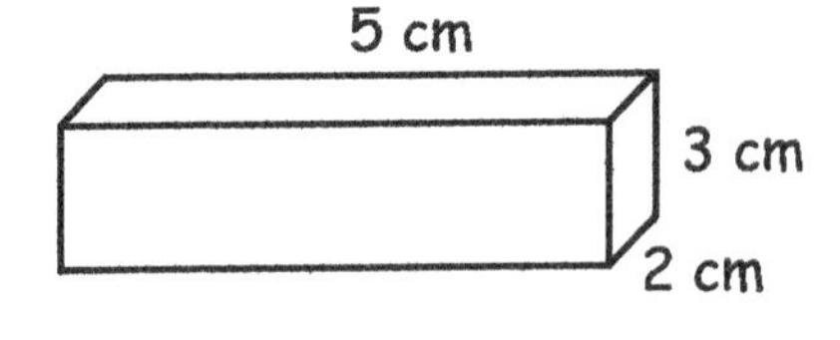

15. $20{,}000 - 16{,}733 = ?$

16. Nathan has 6 feet 4 inches of rope. George has 80 inches of rope. Who has more rope? How much more?

17. On a Fahrenheit thermometer, water boils at ______________.

18. Give the estimated product of 234 and 467.

19. How many millimeters are in 5 meters?

20. Two figures with the same size and shape are ______________.

1.	2.	3.	4.
5.	6.	7.	8.
9.	10.	11.	12.
13.	14.	15.	16.
17.	18.	19.	20.

Lesson #37

1. Numbers with only 2 factors are called __________ numbers.
2. Draw a right angle.
3. Find the LCM of 9 and 14.
4. Which digit is in the ten millions place in 75,908,134?
5. The freezing temperature of water on the Celsius scale is ________.
6. What is the probability of rolling a number greater than two on one roll of a die?

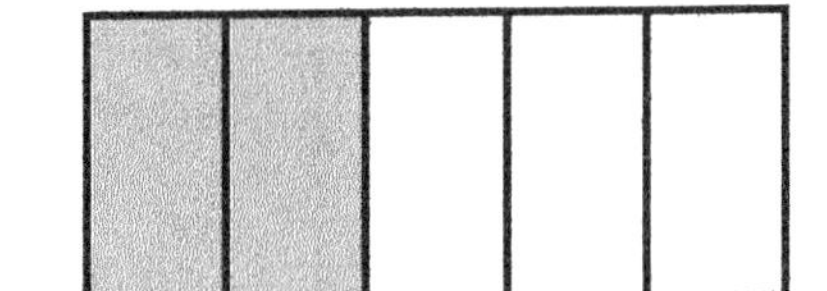

7. What fraction of the shape is not shaded?
8. 546,723 + 498,364 = ?
9. List the factors of 16.

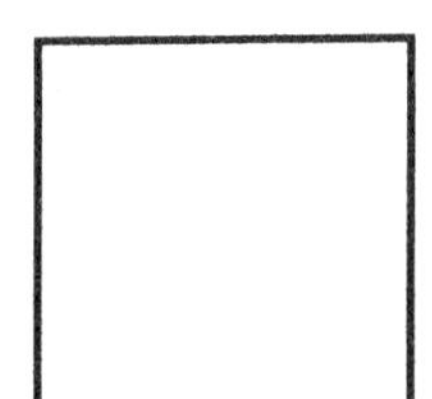

10. 902 – 279 = ?
11. Find the area of the square.
12. Make a factor tree for 48.
13. $74 \times 22 = ?$
14. How many feet are in 7 yards?
15. Half of the diameter of a circle is called the ________________.
16. Find the average of 31, 34, 34, 35 and 36.
17. What is the mode of the set of numbers in #16?
18. $6{,}020 \div 6 = ?$
19. Write $\frac{8}{12}$ in simplest form.
20. a) Give the total sales over the five months.

    b) When was the greatest drop in sales?

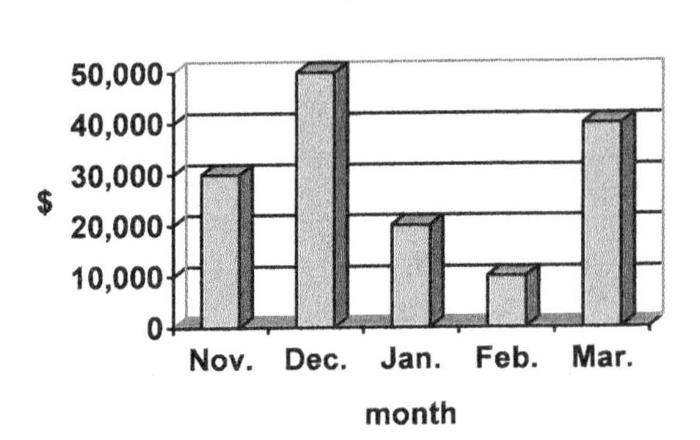

1.	2.	3.	4.
5.	6.	7.	8.
9.	10.	11.	12.
13.	14.	15.	16.
17.	18.	19.	20.

Lesson #38

1. Draw perpendicular lines.

2. What is the perimeter of a rectangle with a length of 14 meters and a width of 7 meters?

3. 
$756 \div 63 = ?$

4. Find the GCF of 12 and 18.

5. How many feet are in 3 miles?

6. $8.1 + 33.6 = ?$

7. Make a factor tree for 42.

8. Write $\frac{8}{24}$ in simplest form.

9. Round 17,946,213 to the nearest million.

10. What do you call a number with more than 2 factors?

11. $80{,}000 - 55{,}632 = ?$

12. Find the volume of the figure.

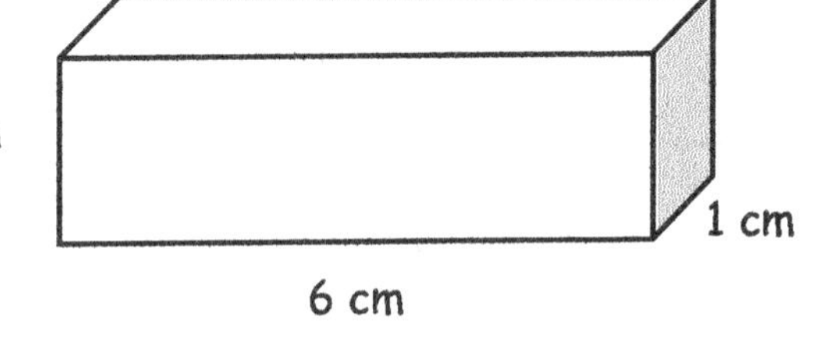

13. 
$12{,}560 \times 3 = ?$

14. Draw two congruent squares.

15. Find the range of 41, 93, 77, 12 and 105.

16. Which is greater, 36 inches or 2 yards?

17. How many centimeters are in 9 meters?

18. Liz has $25. She has 9 bills altogether. She only has $5 bills and $1 bills. How many of each does Liz have?

19. A quadrilateral has ___________ sides.

20. Which digit is in the ten thousands place in 6,947,301?

1.	2.	3.	4.
5.	6.	7.	8.
9.	10.	11.	12.
13.	14.	15.	16.
17.	18.	19.	20.

Lesson #39

1. If it is 7:10 now, what time will it be in 4 hours and 20 minutes?

2. $88 \times 25 = ?$

3. Rename $\frac{10}{15}$ in simplest form.

4. Draw an obtuse angle.

5. Is this figure a polygon? 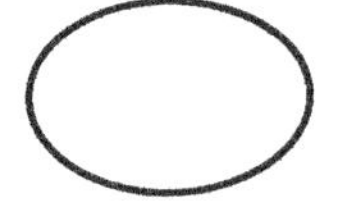

6. $88 \div 25 = ?$

7. Find the LCM of 8 and 15.

8. Find the area of the quadrilateral.

15 in

5 in

9. Is 56 a prime or a composite number?

10. How many millimeters are in 6 meters?

11. If the diameter of a circle is 22 cm, what is the radius?

12. The __________ is the answer in a subtraction problem.

13. Find the median of 49, 52, 13, 33 and 65.

14. List the factors of 30.

15. $618 + 469 = ?$

16. $756 \times 4 = ?$

17. $90.5 - 66.7 = ?$

18. Make a factor tree for 35.

19. Dan exercises 10 minutes every day for the first week. If he doubles his daily exercise time each week, how many minutes per day will he be exercising at the end of four weeks?

20. How many ounces are in 9 pounds?

1.	2.	3.	4.
5.	6.	7.	8.
9.	10.	11.	12.
13.	14.	15.	16.
17.	18.	19.	20.

Lesson #40

1. Make a factor tree for 70.

2. An angle that measures less than 90° is called ____________.

3. Round 38,204,516 to the nearest thousand.

4. $565 \div 25 = ?$

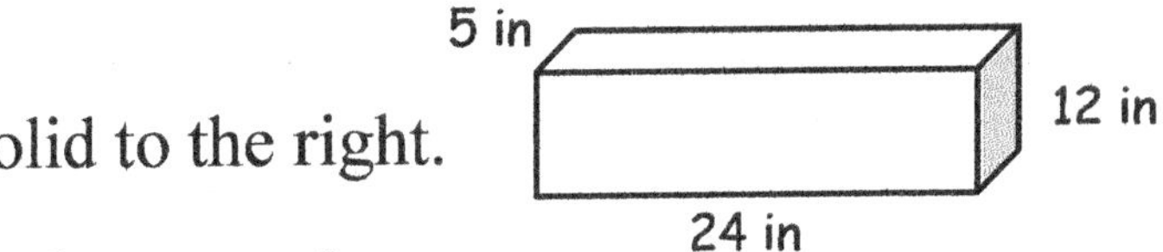

5. Find the volume of the solid to the right.

6. What time is 9 minutes before noon?

7. What is a number with more than 2 factors called?

8. Write the odd numbers between 70 and 78.

9. List the factors of 10.

10. Draw a pentagon.

11. Reduce $\frac{12}{16}$ to simplest form.

12. $500 \times 300 = ?$

13. How many pints are in 4 quarts?

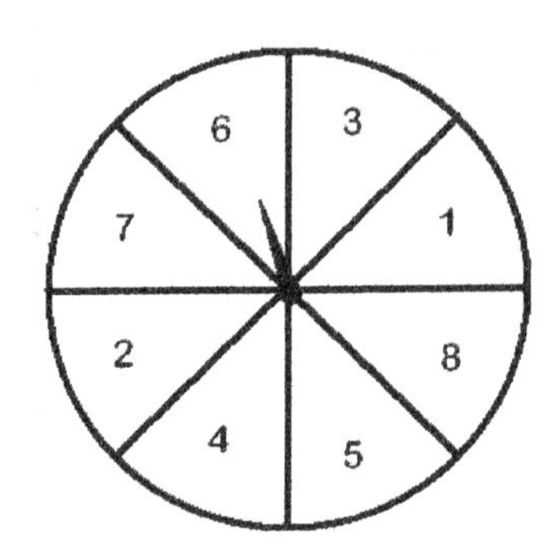

14. What is the probability that the spinner will land on an even number? A number greater than 4?

15. $900 - 467 = ?$

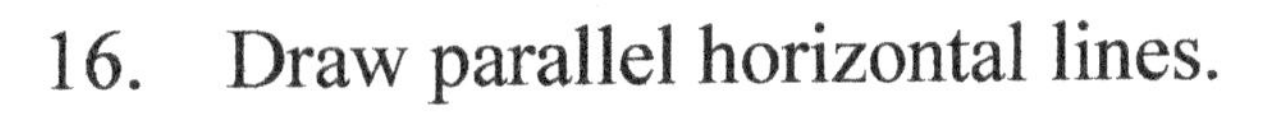

16. Draw parallel horizontal lines.

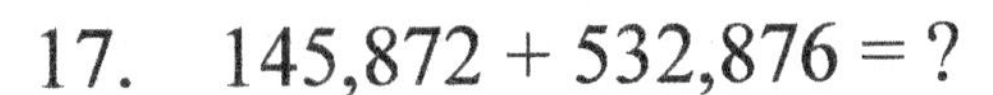

17. $145{,}872 + 532{,}876 = ?$

18. $471.92 + 216.7 = ?$

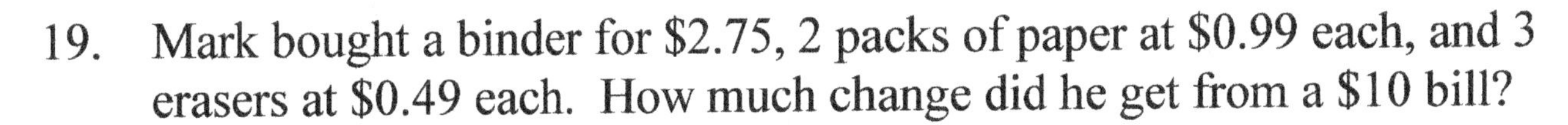

19. Mark bought a binder for $2.75, 2 packs of paper at $0.99 each, and 3 erasers at $0.49 each. How much change did he get from a $10 bill?

20. Draw a circle and shade $\frac{4}{6}$ of it.

1.	2.	3.	4.
5.	6.	7.	8.
9.	10.	11.	12.
13.	14.	15.	16.
17.	18.	19.	20.

Lesson #41

1. $72 + 38 + 9 = ?$
2. How many seconds are in 5 minutes?
3. Find the GCF of 10 and 16.
4. Round 7,493,066 to the nearest million.
5. Nick is 4 years younger than Kyle. Kyle is 6 years older than Maria. Maria is 15. How old is Nick?
6. The answer in a multiplication problem is called the ___________.
7. List the factors of 12.

8. $32{,}905 \times 3 = ?$
9. Make a factor tree for 42.
10. $15{,}435 \div 5 = ?$
11. Find the average of 26, 34, 28 and 36.
12. How many degrees are in a straight angle?
13. Draw intersecting lines.
14. $40{,}000 - 22{,}856 = ?$

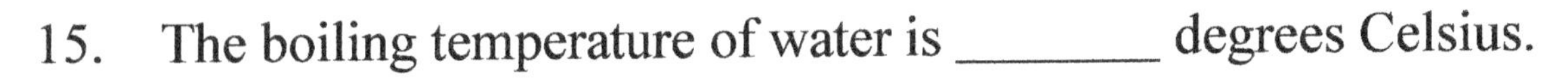

15. The boiling temperature of water is _______ degrees Celsius.
16. Find the area of a square whose sides each measure 9 inches.
17. Write the fraction $\frac{7}{14}$ in simplest form.
18. **An improper fraction has a larger number in the numerator than in the denominator.** *See the Help Pages for examples.*

    Rewrite $\frac{11}{7}$ as a mixed number.
19. How many pounds are 8 tons?
20. Eighty years are _________ decades.

1.	2.	3.	4.
5.	6.	7.	8.
9.	10.	11.	12.
13.	14.	15.	16.
17.	18.	19.	20.

Lesson #42

1. $60 \div 9 = ?$
2. An eight-sided polygon is a(n) ___________.
3. $18 \times 5 = ?$
4. It is 8:35. What time will it be in 2 hours and 25 minutes?
5. $22 \times 34 = ?$
6. How many feet are in a mile?
7. $735{,}144 + 368{,}921 = ?$
8. Reduce $\frac{7}{21}$ to simplest terms.
9. Draw a vertical line.
10. $8{,}420 - 2{,}756 = ?$
11. 7,675 ◯ 7,762

12. Change the improper fraction $\frac{12}{7}$ to a mixed number.
13. How many centuries are the same as 300 years?
14. List the factors of 24.
15. Make a factor tree for 36.
16. Terrance is 5 feet 7 inches tall. What is Terrance's height in inches?
17. On the Fahrenheit scale, water freezes at ____________.
18. Write the next 2 numbers in the sequence. 32, 50, 68, ...
19. $18.44 + 26.78 = ?$
20. Ben's dog weighs 15 pounds 4 ounces. Jeremy's dog weighs 336 ounces. Whose dog weighs the most?

1.	2.	3.	4.
5.	6.	7.	8.
9.	10.	11.	12.
13.	14.	15.	16.
17.	18.	19.	20.

Lesson #43

1. $18 + \_\_\_\_ = 78$

2. Jason lives 9 blocks from work. How many blocks does Jason walk when he walks to work and back home?

3. $51 \times 63 = ?$

4. Make a factor tree for 40.

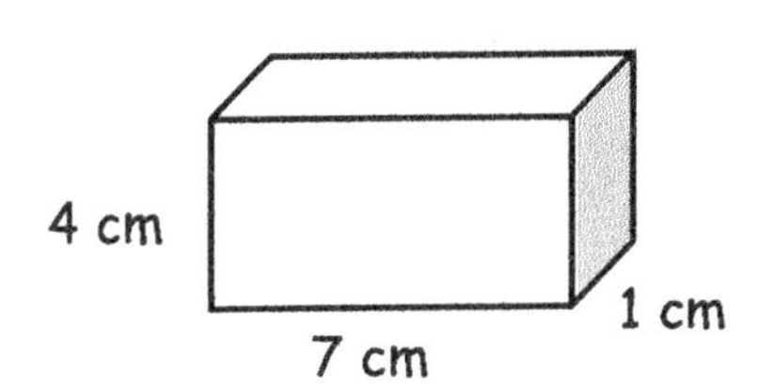

5. Find the volume of the figure.

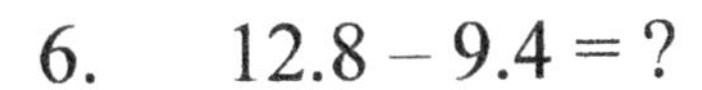

6. $12.8 - 9.4 = ?$

7. Write the first four prime numbers.

8. $26{,}784 \div 2 = ?$

9. Draw 2 congruent hexagons.

10. Round 65,480,726 to the nearest ten million.

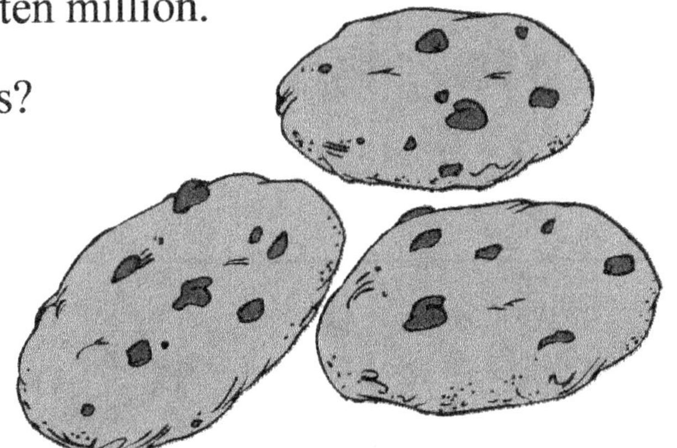

11. How many seconds are in 4 hours?

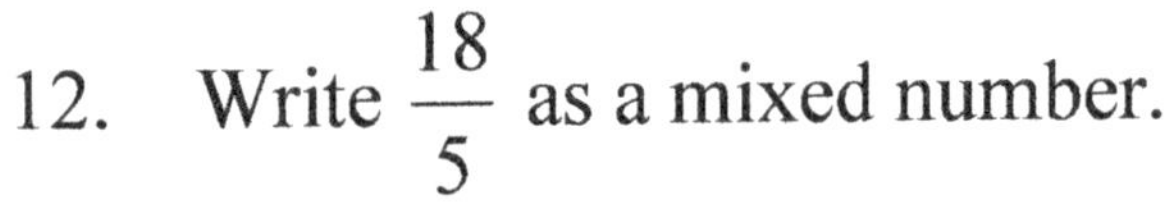

12. Write $\frac{18}{5}$ as a mixed number.

13. $26{,}536 - 19{,}327 = ?$

14. Rewrite $\frac{5}{10}$ in simplest form.

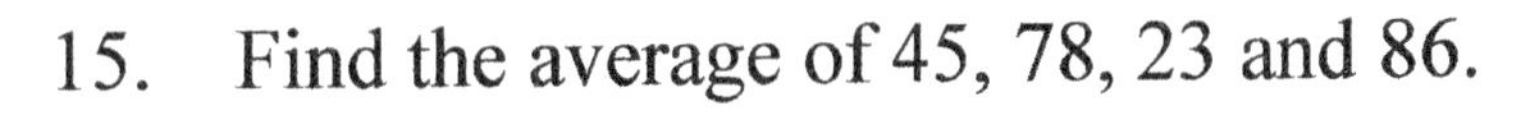

15. Find the average of 45, 78, 23 and 86.

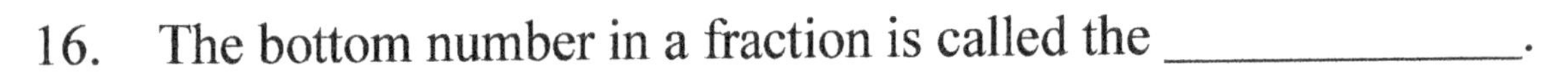

16. The bottom number in a fraction is called the ______________.

17. Find the GCF of 8 and 12.

18. How many grams are in 4 kilograms?

19. List the factors of 18.

20. Maya is baking cookies for a bake sale. Her recipe makes 42 cookies. If Maya makes 16 batches of cookies, what is the estimated number of cookies Maya baked?

1.	2.	3.	4.
5.	6.	7.	8.
9.	10.	11.	12.
13.	14.	15.	16.
17.	18.	19.	20.

Lesson #44

1. Six centuries are ______________ years.

2. 673,448 + 298,215 = ?

3. Put $\frac{6}{12}$ in simplest form.

4. Draw a ray.

5. Round 26,831,907 to the nearest hundred thousand.

6. There are 24 baseball cards in a package. Myron bought 8 packages. How many baseball cards did he buy?

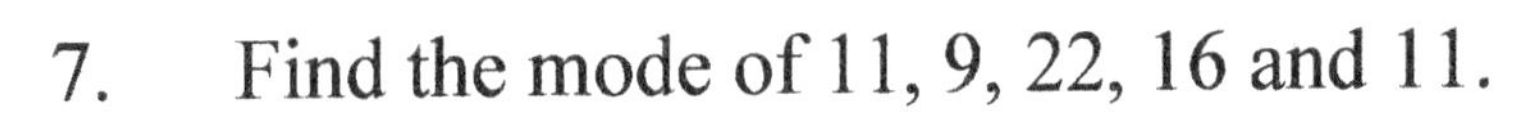

7. Find the mode of 11, 9, 22, 16 and 11.

8. 7,000 – 2,883 = ?

9. What time is 20 minutes before noon?

10. Write $\frac{22}{5}$ as a mixed number.

11. 63 × 51 = ?

12. 24,890 ÷ 6 = ?

13. Find the LCM of 12 and 14.

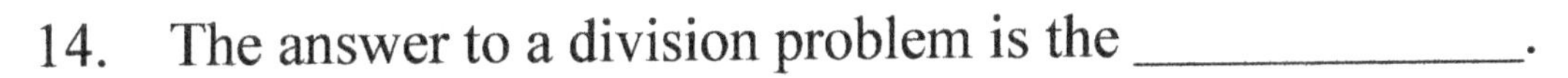

14. The answer to a division problem is the ______________.

15. How many millimeters are in 4 meters?

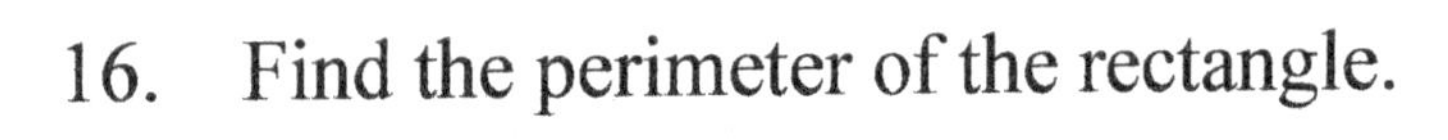

16. Find the perimeter of the rectangle.

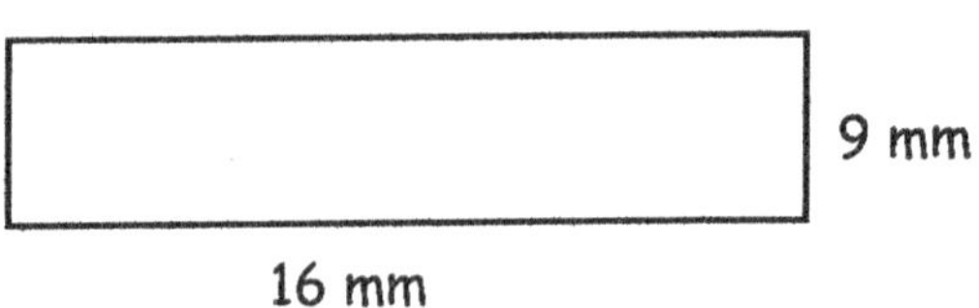

17. 62.5 – 36.8 = ?

18. Find the average of 657, 890 and 1,240.

19. On the Celsius scale, water freezes at ___________.

20. List the factors of 14.

1.	2.	3.	4.
5.	6.	7.	8.
9.	10.	11.	12.
13.	14.	15.	16.
17.	18.	19.	20.

Lesson #45

1. What do you call a number that has only 2 factors?
2. A six-sided polygon is called a(n) ______________.
3. **A mixed number can be changed to an improper fraction.** *See the Help Pages for examples.* Write $3\frac{4}{7}$ as an improper fraction.

4. Which is greater, 180 minutes or 2 hours?
5. How many degrees are in a straight angle?
6. $6{,}315 \times 6 = ?$
7. $505 - 178 = ?$
8. Make a factor tree for 42.
9. Reduce $\frac{4}{12}$ to simplest form.

10. How many teaspoons are in 6 tablespoons?

11. Round 13,509,796 to the nearest hundred.
12. $655 \div 3 = ?$

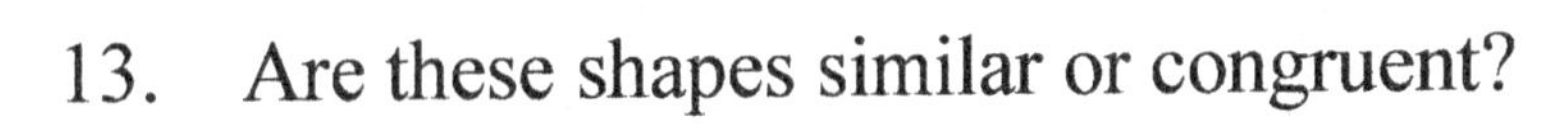

13. Are these shapes similar or congruent?
14. $421 + 858 + 92 = ?$

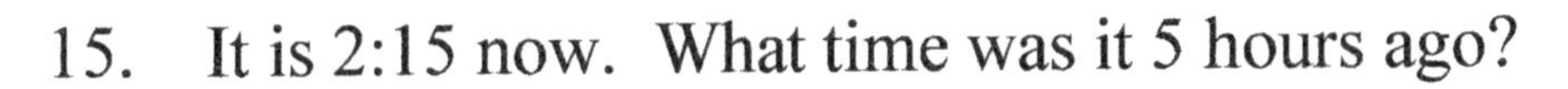

15. It is 2:15 now. What time was it 5 hours ago?

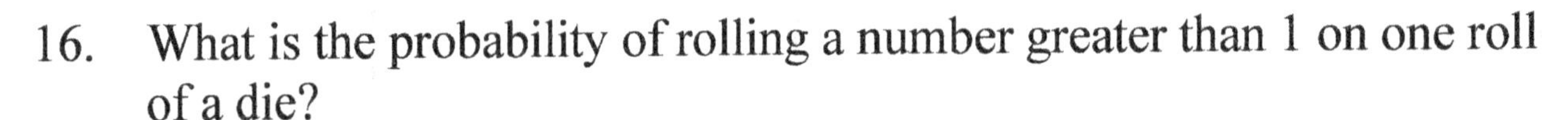

16. What is the probability of rolling a number greater than 1 on one roll of a die?
17. Write $\frac{34}{6}$ as a mixed number.
18. If the diameter of a circle is 24 mm, what is the radius?
19. $22.36 + 19.55 = ?$
20. How many decades are 90 years?

1.	2.	3.	4.
5.	6.	7.	8.
9.	10.	11.	12.
13.	14.	15.	16.
17.	18.	19.	20.

Lesson #46

1. Find the mode of 37, 92, 56, 19 and 56.

2. Write $\frac{6}{9}$ in simplest form.

3. The answer to an addition problem is called the ___________.

4. Write $\frac{47}{5}$ as a mixed number.

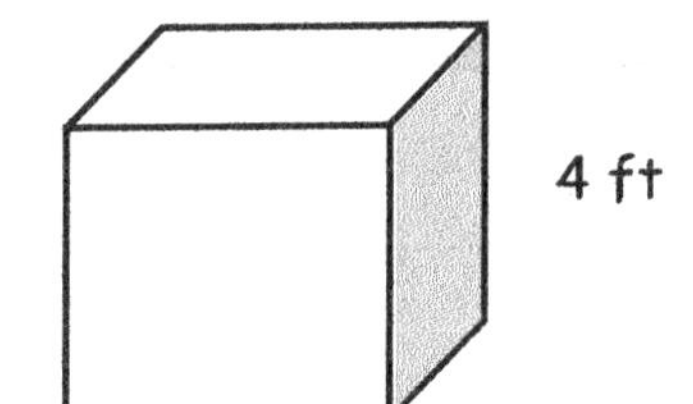

5. Find the volume of the cube.

6. How many pints are in 5 quarts?

7. 9,478 ◯ 9,784

8. List the factors of 8.

9. Give the estimated difference of 3,456 and 1,867.

10. Write $6\frac{2}{5}$ as an improper fraction.

11. How many feet are in 3 miles?

12. $25,816 + 67,063 = ?$

13. $56 \times 12 = ?$

14. $936 \div 25 = ?$

15. Find the GCF of 16 and 24.

16. Draw perpendicular lines.

17. Make a factor tree for 24.

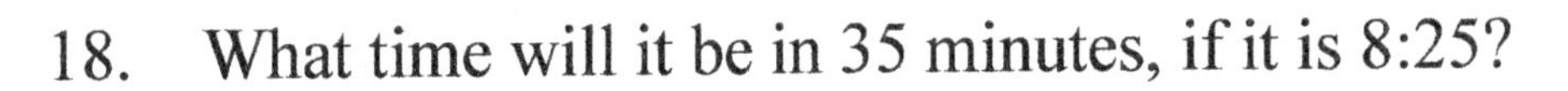

18. What time will it be in 35 minutes, if it is 8:25?

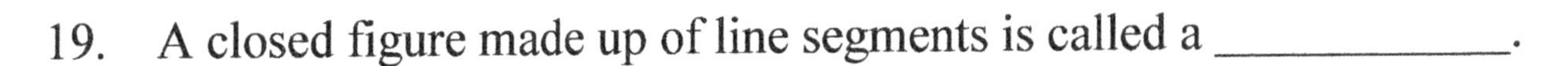

19. A closed figure made up of line segments is called a ___________.

20. Is the number 71 a prime or composite number?

1.	2.	3.	4.
5.	6.	7.	8.
9.	10.	11.	12.
13.	14.	15.	16.
17.	18.	19.	20.

Lesson #47

1. List the factors of 24.
2. Find the range of 87, 42, 65, 110 and 33.
3. $34 \times 27 = ?$
4. Find the volume of the solid.

5. $286 \div 40 = ?$
6. How many quarts are in 12 gallons?
7. Draw intersecting lines.
8. Write $\frac{27}{4}$ as a mixed number.
9. At 45 minutes after 3:00, what time is it?
10. The school is purchasing new curtains for each classroom. There are 27 classrooms and each room needs 8 curtain panels. What is the estimated number of curtain panels the school will need to buy?
11. $19.9 - 12.4 = ?$
12. Put $\frac{15}{25}$ in simplest form.
13. Which digit is in the hundred thousands place in 76,219,543?
14. Change $7\frac{2}{3}$ to an improper fraction.
15. On a Celsius thermometer, water boils at ____________.
16. Find the LCM of 14 and 20.
17. Does a houseplant need about 300 ml or 300 L of water at one time?
18. $175{,}416 + 249{,}732 = ?$
19. How many centimeters are 8 meters?
20. $6 \times 9 = ?$

1.	2.	3.	4.
5.	6.	7.	8.
9.	10.	11.	12.
13.	14.	15.	16.
17.	18.	19.	20.

Lesson #48

1. Is the number 19 a prime or a composite number?

2. 90,000 – 39,471 = ?

3. Find the area of a square whose sides each measure 6 feet.

4. 80 × 24 = ?

5. How many cups are in 5 pints?

6. Reduce $\frac{4}{20}$ to simplest form.

7. Draw a line segment.

8. Write $8\frac{3}{4}$ as an improper fraction.

9. 352 + 386 = ?

10. Round 54,857,231 to the nearest million.

11. The top number in a fraction is called the ___________.

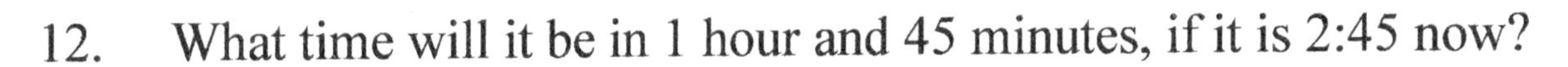

12. What time will it be in 1 hour and 45 minutes, if it is 2:45 now?

13. 148 ÷ 37 = ?

14. Change $\frac{52}{8}$ to a mixed number.

15. Draw a right angle.

16. If the radius of a circle is 18 mm, what is the diameter?

17. Nine dozen cupcakes will be divided evenly among 4 classrooms. How many cupcakes will each classroom receive?

18. Find the GCF of 12 and 18.

19. Figures with the same size and shape are ____________.

20. How many feet are in 7 yards?

1.	2.	3.	4.
5.	6.	7.	8.
9.	10.	11.	12.
13.	14.	15.	16.
17.	18.	19.	20.

Lesson #49

1. Draw a hexagon.
2. Find the GCF of 14 and 21.
3. Change $9\frac{4}{5}$ to an improper fraction.
4. Round 245,718,206 to the nearest ten million.
5. How many inches are in 7 feet?
6. Write $\frac{19}{5}$ as a mixed number.
7. 15,736 + 58,144 = ?
8. Find the area of the square.

12 in

9. 36,054 ÷ 6 = ?

10. How many cups are in 4 pints?

11. Draw perpendicular lines.
12. Estimate the product of 56 and 32.
13. Find the missing numerator. $\frac{5}{7} = \frac{?}{21}$
14. 5,071 – 3,698 = ?
15. Put $\frac{12}{24}$ in simplest form.

16. Figures having the same shape, but different size are ________.
17. Which is less, 3 gallons or 9 quarts?
18. 39,210 × 3 = ?
19. The sum of two numbers is 17. Their product is 60. What are the numbers?
20. List the factors of 18.

1.	2.	3.	4.
5.	6.	7.	8.
9.	10.	11.	12.
13.	14.	15.	16.
17.	18.	19.	20.

Lesson #50

1. How many degrees are in a straight angle?
2. If the diameter of a circle is 20 mm, what is the radius?
3. Find the volume of this solid figure.

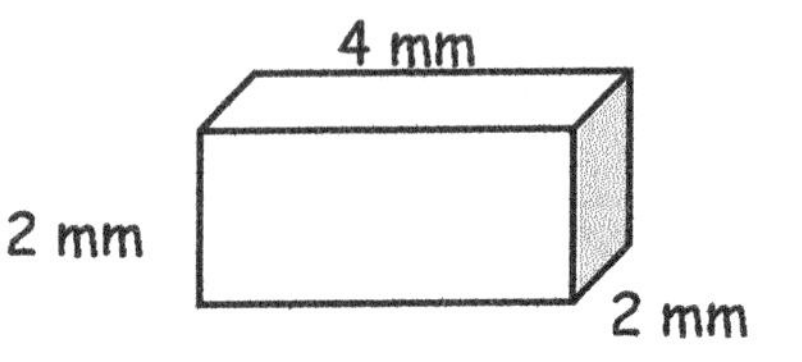

4. Find the LCM of 20 and 32.
5. $2{,}546 \times 2 = ?$
6. On a Celsius thermometer, water boils at ____________.
7. Make a factor tree for 64.
8. $524 + 198 + 611 = ?$
9. Find the missing numerator. $\frac{4}{9} = \frac{?}{45}$
10. Find the range of 93, 20, 88 and 16.
11. How many millimeters are in 5 meters?
12. $4{,}230 \div 6 = ?$
13. Draw a line segment.
14. $7.2 + 4.9 = ?$
15. Change $\frac{8}{24}$ to simplest form.

16. Find the perimeter of an octagon whose sides measure 6 cm each.
17. A car averages 27 miles to the gallon. If its tank holds 15 gallons of gasoline, how far can the car drive on one tank of gas?
18. $80{,}000 - 48{,}253 = ?$
19. What is the middle number in an ordered set of numbers called?
20. Write $\frac{23}{5}$ as a mixed number.

1.	2.	3.	4.
5.	6.	7.	8.
9.	10.	11.	12.
13.	14.	15.	16.
17.	18.	19.	20.

Lesson #51

1. Change $5\frac{5}{6}$ to an improper fraction.
2. Draw an acute angle.
3. 563,209 + 496,771 = ?
4. The answer to a division problem is the ______________.
5. Find the GCF of 12 and 14.
6. Write the next number in the sequence. 13, 39, 117, ...
7. Which digit is in the hundred millions place in 319,027,846?
8. Find the area of a square if one side measures 14 inches.
9. How many minutes are in 7 hours?
10. If it is 1:40 now, what time was it 4 hours and 10 minutes ago?
11. Write $\frac{42}{8}$ as a mixed number.
12. Make a factor tree for 50.
13. $39 \times 53 = ?$
14. $420 \div 70 = ?$
15. $8,005 - 2,644 = ?$
16. Write $\frac{8}{16}$ in simplest terms.
17. Find the missing numerator. $\frac{5}{8} = \frac{?}{40}$
18. The bottom number in a fraction is called the ______________.
19. Round 4,213,772 to the nearest million.
20. Aunt Dora bought a 20-lb turkey at \$0.89 per pound. She also bought a bag of potatoes for \$1.59, and 3 pumpkin pies for \$2.59 each. How much change did she get back from \$40?

1.	2.	3.	4.
5.	6.	7.	8.
9.	10.	11.	12.
13.	14.	15.	16.
17.	18.	19.	20.

Lesson #52

1. Find the perimeter of a hexagon whose sides measure 7 mm.

2. $430 \times 22 = ?$

3. $6.23 + 4.6 = ?$

4. List the factors of 10.

5. Find the median and the mode of 64, 41, 30, 17 and 41.

6. $30{,}000 - 12{,}657 = ?$

7. Draw perpendicular lines.

8. Write $\frac{31}{5}$ as a mixed number.

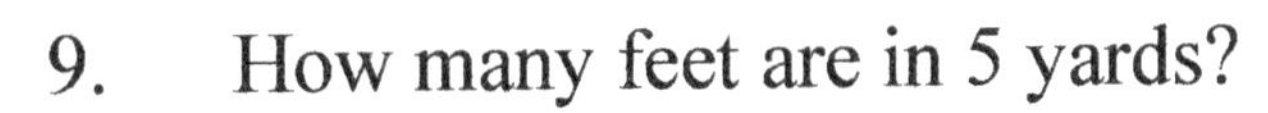

9. How many feet are in 5 yards?

10. Make a factor tree for 56.

11. $9{,}356 \div 4 = ?$

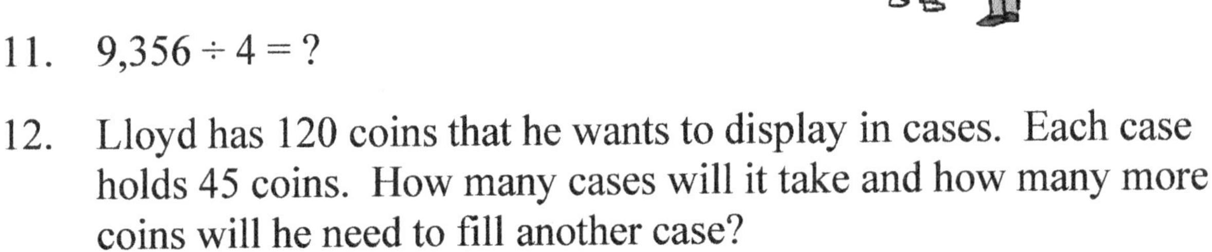

12. Lloyd has 120 coins that he wants to display in cases. Each case holds 45 coins. How many cases will it take and how many more coins will he need to fill another case?

13. Is 47 a prime or a composite number?

14. Compare. $\frac{4}{7} \bigcirc \frac{2}{5}$ *See the Help Pages for examples.*

15. Write the fraction $\frac{6}{24}$ in simplest form.

16. Write $4\frac{2}{7}$ as an improper fraction.

17. Which is greater, 9 quarters or \$2?

18. What is located at (4, 1)?

19. What is located at (1, 1)?

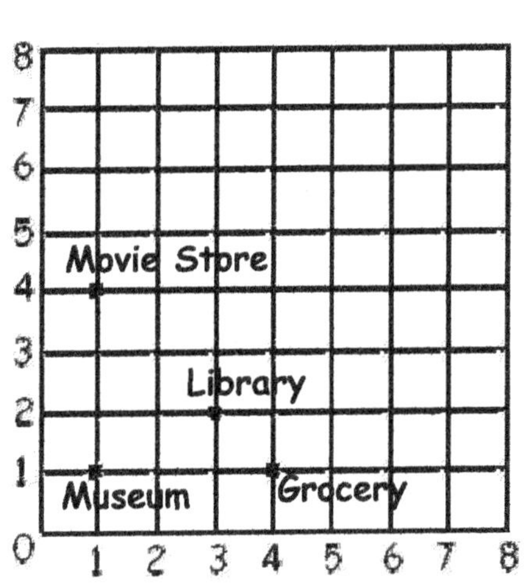

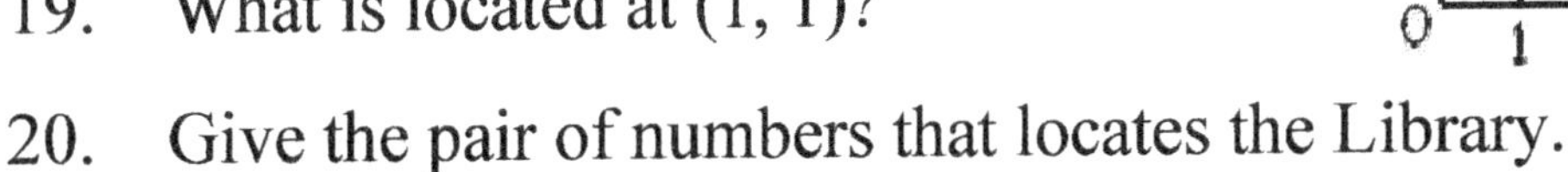

20. Give the pair of numbers that locates the Library.

1.	2.	3.	4.
5.	6.	7.	8.
9.	10.	11.	12.
13.	14.	15.	16.
17.	18.	19.	20.

Lesson #53

1. Rewrite $\frac{3}{21}$ in simplest form.
2. If it's six minutes before 2:00, what time is it?
3. Change $8\frac{3}{4}$ to an improper fraction.
4. What is the volume of the rectangular solid?

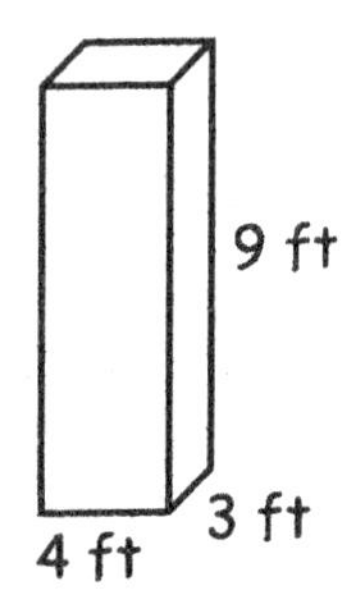

5. $31.8 - 17.6 = ?$
6. Find the LCM of 9 and 15.
7. On a Fahrenheit thermometer, water boils at ______________.
8. $2{,}679 + 9{,}661 = ?$
9. What is the probability of rolling an even number on 1 roll of a die?
10. $\frac{7}{8} \bigcirc \frac{5}{6}$
11. $44 \times 22 = ?$
12. Write $\frac{38}{7}$ as a mixed number.
13. Draw intersecting lines.

14. What do you call the number that is left over after one number is divided into another number?
15. Which digit is in the millions place in 836,025,174?
16. How many grams are in 3 kilograms?
17. Find the range of 68, 105, 13 and 44.
18. An eight-sided polygon is a(n) ______________.
19. $703 - 248 = ?$
20. Mrs. Jefferson is making punch. The recipe calls for 1 gallon of liquid. If she has already added 2 pints and 1 quart, how many more quarts does she have to add?

1.	2.	3.	4.
5.	6.	7.	8.
9.	10.	11.	12.
13.	14.	15.	16.
17.	18.	19.	20.

Lesson #54

1. What do you call a number with only 2 factors?

2. How many months are in 5 years?

3. Find the perimeter of a square whose sides measure 4 feet each.

4. $84 \times 41 = ?$

5. Find the missing denominator. $\frac{4}{9} = \frac{16}{?}$

6. Is 42 a prime or a composite number?

7. $20.5 - 12.8 = ?$

8. Reduce $\frac{9}{27}$ to simplest terms.

9. Round 43,165,251 to the nearest million.

10. $764 + 258 = ?$

11. Write $2\frac{4}{5}$ as an improper fraction.

12. $4{,}210 - 1{,}476 = ?$

13. What will the time be at 40 minutes after 9:00?

14. Change $\frac{28}{5}$ to a mixed number.

15. Find the volume of this solid figure.

3 cm
4 cm
6 cm

16. How many degrees are in a straight angle?

17. 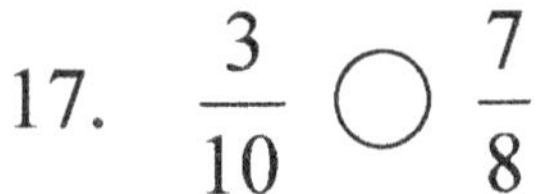
$\frac{3}{10} \bigcirc \frac{7}{8}$

18. How many pounds are in 8 tons?

19. Make a factor tree for 20.

20. A can of paint covers 400 square feet. If Seth needs to cover 2,400 square feet, how many cans of paint will he have to buy?

1.	2.	3.	4.
5.	6.	7.	8.
9.	10.	11.	12.
13.	14.	15.	16.
17.	18.	19.	20.

Lesson #55

1. Round 38,215,077 to the nearest ten thousand.

2. Find the GCF of 10 and 25.

3. Make a factor tree for 90.

4. If the diameter of a circle is 14 mm, what is the radius?

5. $235 \times 12 = ?$

6. List the factors of 12.

7. Write $9\frac{7}{9}$ as an improper fraction.

8. $\frac{5}{7} \bigcirc \frac{4}{9}$

9. $50{,}000 - 29{,}175 = ?$

10. $\frac{7}{8} - \frac{3}{8} = ?$

11. Find the missing numerator. $\frac{6}{7} = \frac{?}{42}$

12. How many feet are in 2 miles?

13. $850 \div 70 = ?$

14. Write 64,275 in expanded form.

15. A rectangular swimming pool is 6 ft deep, 14 ft wide and 32 feet long. What is the volume of the swimming pool?

16. Draw a line of symmetry on the hexagon.

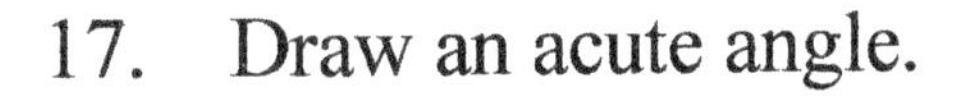

17. Draw an acute angle.

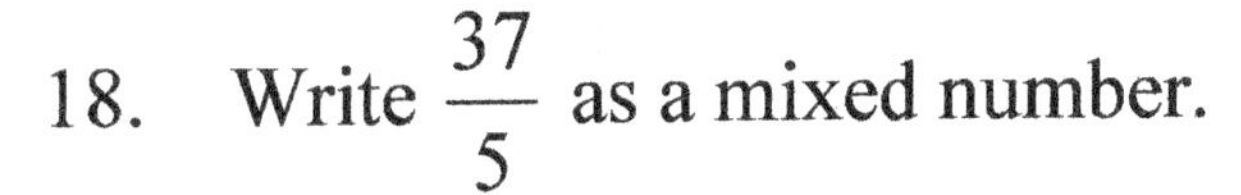

18. Write $\frac{37}{5}$ as a mixed number.

19. How many centimeters are in 9 meters?

20. $437{,}628 + 857{,}293 = ?$

1.	2.	3.	4.
5.	6.	7.	8.
9.	10.	11.	12.
13.	14.	15.	16.
17.	18.	19.	20.

Lesson #56

1. On the Fahrenheit scale, water freezes at ___________.

2. $93 + 24 + 16 = ?$

3. Round 431,210,856 to the nearest ten million.

4. $35 \times 32 = ?$

5. Make a factor tree for 27.

6. $480 \div 40 = ?$

7. Find the area of the square.

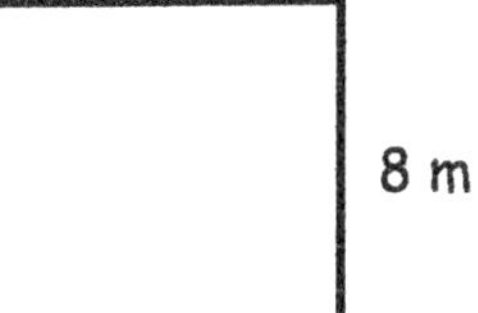

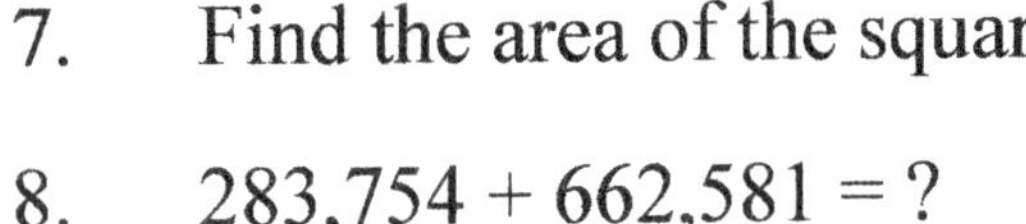

8. $283{,}754 + 662{,}581 = ?$

9. The middle number in a set of numbers is the ____________.

10. Two figures with the same size and shape are ________.

11. $\frac{2}{5} = \frac{?}{30}$

12. $8{,}230 - 5{,}726 = ?$

13. $\frac{3}{5} \bigcirc \frac{4}{9}$

14. How many ounces are in 2 pounds?

15. Draw 2 similar hexagons.

16. Write $3\frac{7}{9}$ as an improper fraction.

17. Which digit is in the hundred thousands place in 35,761,042?

18. What is the probability of rolling a four on one roll of a die?

19. Denise was cutting 7-foot lengths of ribbon. How many lengths can she make from 65 feet of ribbon?

20. How many teaspoons are in 5 tablespoons?

1.	2.	3.	4.
5.	6.	7.	8.
9.	10.	11.	12.
13.	14.	15.	16.
17.	18.	19.	20.

Lesson #57

1. Find the LCM of 15 and 18.

2. $\frac{8}{9} = \frac{48}{?}$

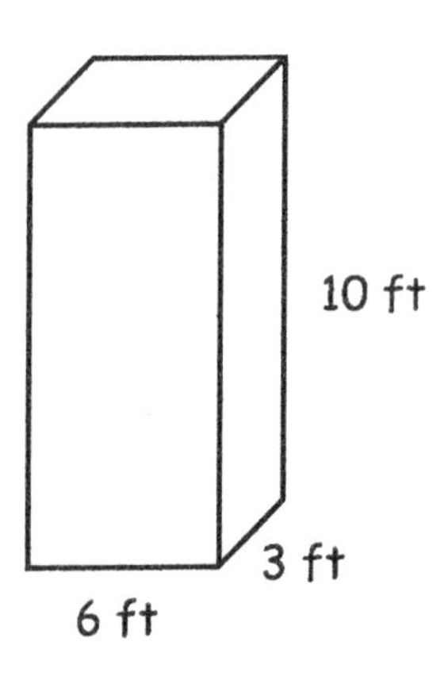

3. Find the volume of the rectangular prism.

4. Draw parallel horizontal lines.

5. 73,219 + 49,634 = ?

6. How many pints are in 7 quarts?

7. $43 \times 51 = ?$

8. Round 162,816,753 to the nearest thousand.

9. What do you call a number with more than 2 factors?

10. The answer to a division problem is called the ___________.

11. Write $\frac{9}{36}$ in simplest form.

12. $\frac{8}{11} \bigcirc \frac{9}{10}$

13. $800 - 279 = ?$

14. $\frac{3}{10} + \frac{4}{10} = ?$

15. How many tons are 8,000 pounds?

16. $7{,}236 \div 60 = ?$

17. Find the range of 83, 70, 21, 48 and 116.

18. On a Fahrenheit thermometer, water boils at ___________.

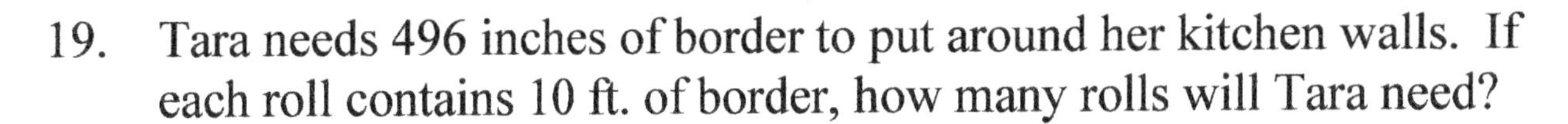

19. Tara needs 496 inches of border to put around her kitchen walls. If each roll contains 10 ft. of border, how many rolls will Tara need?

20. Write $7\frac{2}{3}$ as an improper fraction.

1.	2.	3.	4.
5.	6.	7.	8.
9.	10.	11.	12.
13.	14.	15.	16.
17.	18.	19.	20.

Lesson #58

1. How many feet are in 3 miles?
2. A polygon with four sides is called a(n) ____________.
3. Draw a right angle.
4. Find the perimeter of this rectangle.

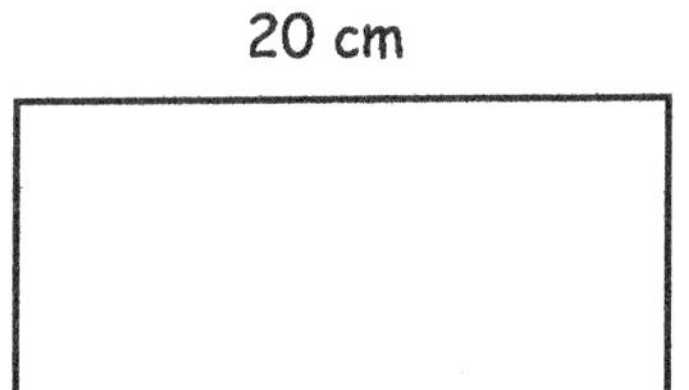

5. Write 375,829 in expanded form.
6. $76{,}344 + 88{,}154 = ?$
7. Round 2,451,913 to the nearest ten thousand.
8. If Darrin is 5 feet 5 inches tall, what is his height in inches?
9. Which digit is in the ten millions place in 35,698,021?
10. Make a factor tree for 54.

11. $\frac{4}{5} - \frac{1}{5} = ?$
12. $\frac{3}{8} = \frac{?}{64}$
13. $50{,}000 - 33{,}651 = ?$
14. $332 \times 23 = ?$
15. Find the GCF of 12 and 16.
16. Write $\frac{6}{24}$ in simplest form.
17. $2{,}475 \div 5 = ?$
18. Thomas is saving the same amount each month for 2 years to buy a T.V. that costs $792. How much does he save each month?
19. How many quarts are in 8 gallons?
20. $\frac{3}{8} \bigcirc \frac{5}{7}$

1.	2.	3.	4.
5.	6.	7.	8.
9.	10.	11.	12.
13.	14.	15.	16.
17.	18.	19.	20.

Lesson #59

1. Rewrite $\frac{10}{15}$ in simplest terms.

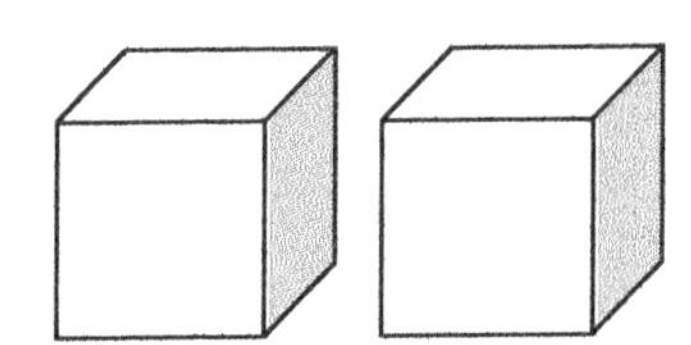

2. Are these shapes congruent?

3. $503{,}472 + 176{,}593 = ?$

4. Find the average and the mode of 12, 13, 22, 13 and 15.

5. $603 - 159 = ?$

6. Round 43,124,567 to the nearest ten thousand.

7. How many inches are in 3 yards?

8. Draw an obtuse angle.

9. $\frac{4}{9} + \frac{4}{9} = ?$

10. $31 \times 25 = ?$

11. How many pints are in 5 quarts?

12. $85{,}156 \div 6 = ?$

13. Find the LCM of 7 and 12.

14. Find the perimeter of this square.

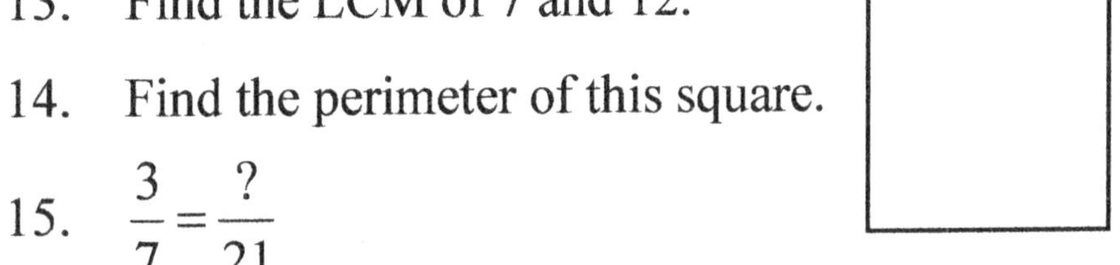

15. $\frac{3}{7} = \frac{?}{21}$

16. If the concert began at 7:15 p.m. and lasted for 1 hour and 45 minutes, at what time did the concert end?

17. Which is greater, 480 seconds or 6 minutes?

18. Write $\frac{65}{9}$ as a mixed number.

19. How many more people bought tacos than hot dogs?

20. What was the total number of meals bought?

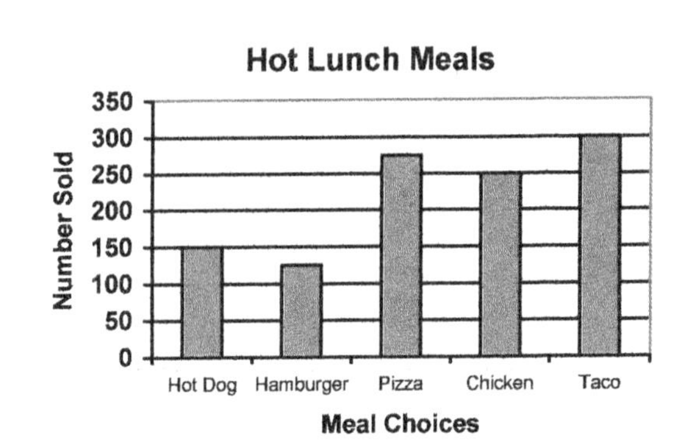

1.	2.	3.	4.
5.	6.	7.	8.
9.	10.	11.	12.
13.	14.	15.	16.
17.	18.	19.	20.

Lesson #60

1. Make a factor tree for 72.
2. How many decades are equal to 70 years?
3. $30{,}000 - 14{,}365 = ?$
4. Find the area of the quadrilateral.

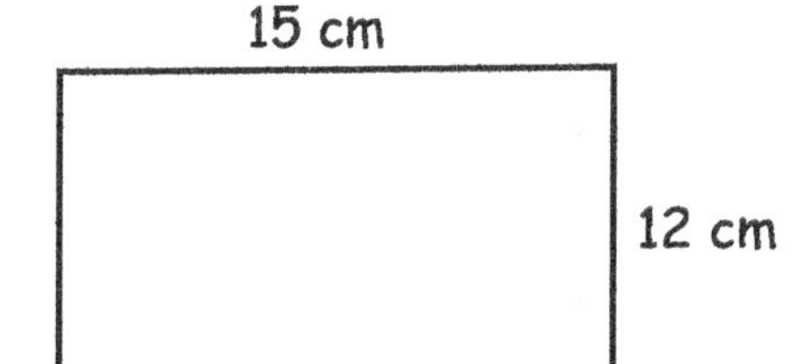

5. $3{,}419 \times 4 = ?$
6. $\frac{5}{8} = \frac{25}{?}$
7. Monica read a 625-page book in five days. What was the average number of pages she read per day?
8. A five-sided polygon is called a(n) ____________.
9. Rewrite $8\frac{4}{7}$ as an improper fraction.

10. $16\frac{9}{10} - 10\frac{4}{10} = ?$
11. Find the range of 95, 80, 120, 44 and 22.
12. Is the fraction $\frac{5}{8}$ in simplest form?
13. $\frac{4}{7} \bigcirc \frac{5}{8}$
14. $45{,}716 + 22{,}739 = ?$
15. Aunt Jo's garden contains 7 rows of plants with 12 plants in each row. How many plants are in Aunt Jo's garden?
16. $\frac{4}{5} + \frac{1}{5} = ?$
17. In a bag of 9 marbles, five are yellow and four are black. What is the probability of picking a black one? A yellow one?
18. How many centimeters are in 5 meters?
19. Draw a ray.
20. What do you call the number that occurs most often in a set of data?

1.	2.	3.	4.
5.	6.	7.	8.
9.	10.	11.	12.
13.	14.	15.	16.
17.	18.	19.	20.

Lesson #61

1. $50 \times 50 = ?$

2. Rewrite $\frac{12}{18}$ in simplest form.

3. $25.7 + 16.92 = ?$

4. $2\frac{1}{5} + 3\frac{2}{5} = ?$

5. $967 \div 32 = ?$

6. List the factors of 20.

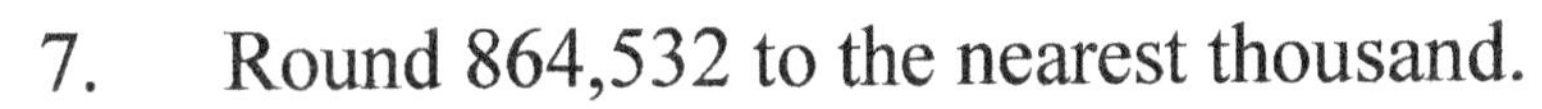

7. Round 864,532 to the nearest thousand.

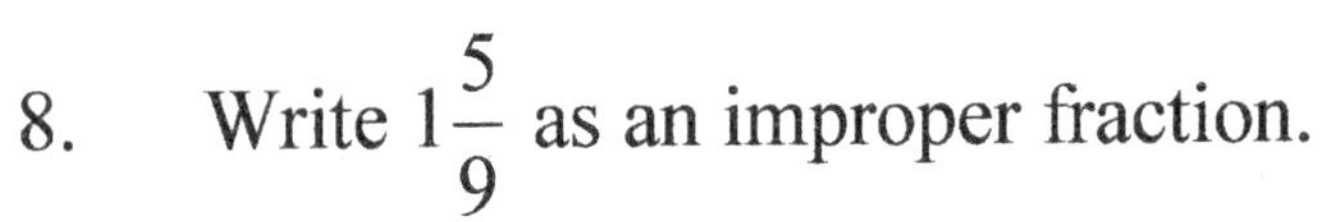

8. Write $1\frac{5}{9}$ as an improper fraction.

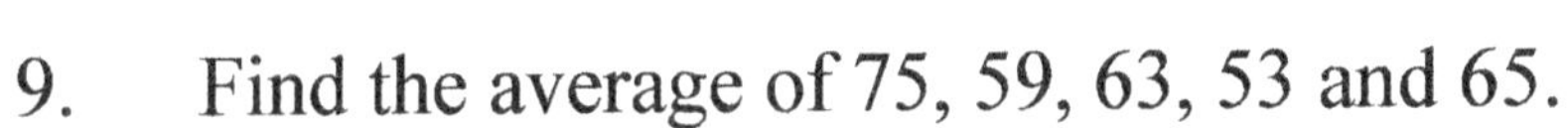

9. Find the average of 75, 59, 63, 53 and 65.

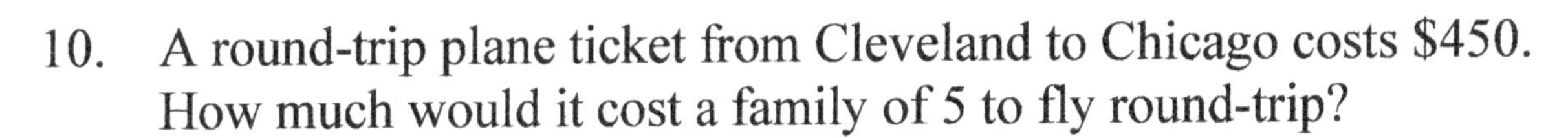

10. A round-trip plane ticket from Cleveland to Chicago costs $450. How much would it cost a family of 5 to fly round-trip?

11. $4,863 \times 7 = ?$

12. Identify this angle by type.

13. $5,005 - 1,431 = ?$

14. Write the formula for finding the area of a quadrilateral.

15. Find the GCF of 21 and 28.

16. $337,805 + 621,215 = ?$

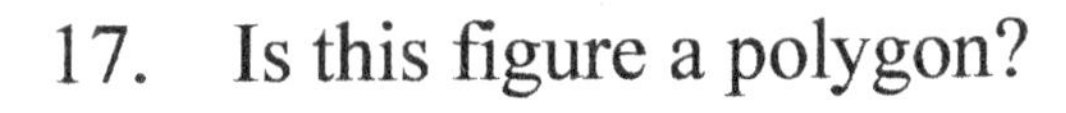

17. Is this figure a polygon?

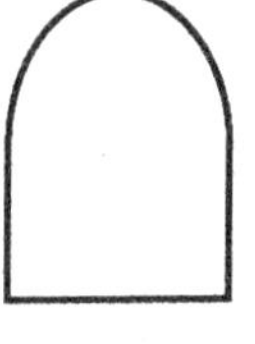

18. $\frac{3}{7} \bigcirc \frac{2}{5}$

19. How many cups are in 2 pints?

20. A fraction whose numerator is larger than its denominator is called a(n) _______________ fraction.

1.	2.	3.	4.
5.	6.	7.	8.
9.	10.	11.	12.
13.	14.	15.	16.
17.	18.	19.	20.

Lesson #62

1. How many days are in 7 weeks?

2. $30 \times 46 = ?$

3. Find the area of the rectangle.

4. $9{,}653 \div 3 = ?$

5. Find the range of 77, 50, 99 and 11.

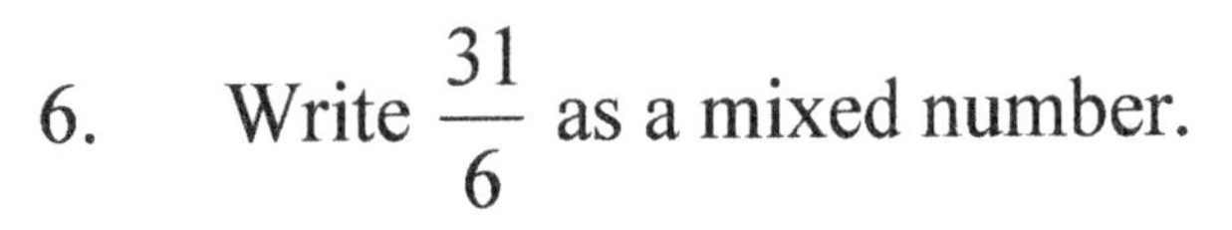

6. Write $\frac{31}{6}$ as a mixed number.

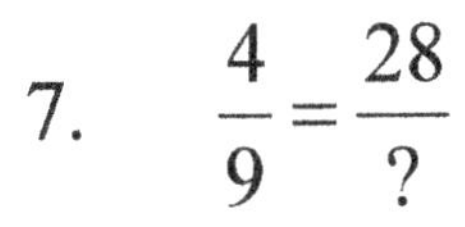

7. $\frac{4}{9} = \frac{28}{?}$

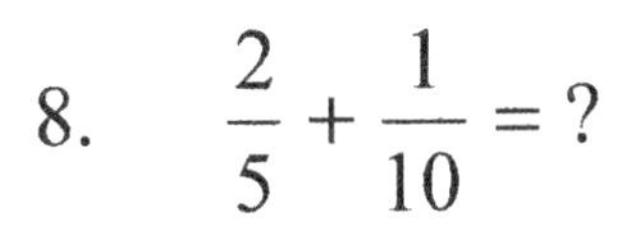

8. $\frac{2}{5} + \frac{1}{10} = ?$

9. Find the LCM of 10 and 12.

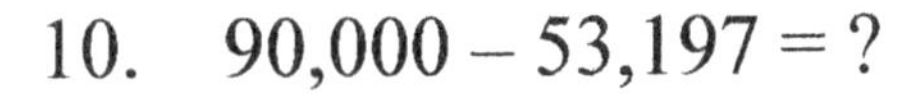

10. $90{,}000 - 53{,}197 = ?$

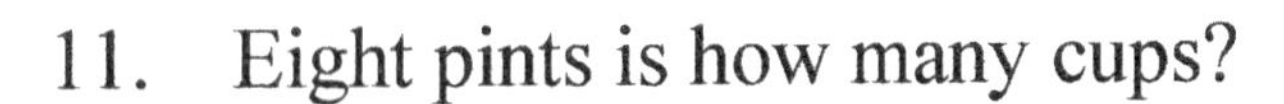

11. Eight pints is how many cups?

12. Which digit is in the hundred thousands place in 15,023,876?

13. Write $7\frac{2}{9}$ as an improper fraction.

14. Is the height of a door closer to 8 feet or 8 yards?

15. What year was it exactly 6 centuries before 1952?

16. The local library wants to fence their property. The property is 78 m long and 65 m wide. How much fencing will they need?

17. $47{,}413 + 29{,}068 = ?$

18. The answer to a multiplication problem is the ________.

19. $81.7 - 26.4 = ?$

20. Write 721,564 in expanded form.

1.	2.	3.	4.
5.	6.	7.	8.
9.	10.	11.	12.
13.	14.	15.	16.
17.	18.	19.	20.

Lesson #63

1. Write the formula for finding the volume of a prism.

2. Write $7\frac{1}{5}$ as an improper fraction.

3. A pentagon has _____ sides.

4. $605 - 258 = ?$

5. $\frac{8}{11} - \frac{3}{11} = ?$

6. Draw intersecting lines.

7. $24 \times 23 = ?$

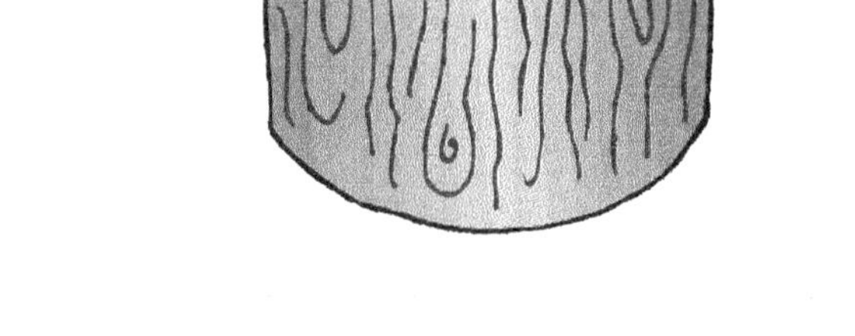

8. Put $\frac{8}{12}$ in simplest form.

9. If it is 2:15 now, what time will it be in 8 hours and 15 minutes?

10. $4,761 \times 5 = ?$

11. The answer to a subtraction problem is called the __________.

12. Yolanda used $\frac{1}{2}$ cup of sugar and $\frac{2}{3}$ cup of milk. How many cups of ingredients did Yolanda use altogether?

13. If the radius of a circle is 10 mm, what is the circle's diameter?

14. List the factors of 12.

15. Find the median of 8, 21, 11, 57 and 39.

16. $\frac{4}{5} = \frac{36}{?}$

17. $17,916 + 14,389 = ?$

18. Make a factor tree for 40.

Write the ordered pair for each fruit.

19. Plum _________ Apple __________

20. Orange_______ Peach __________

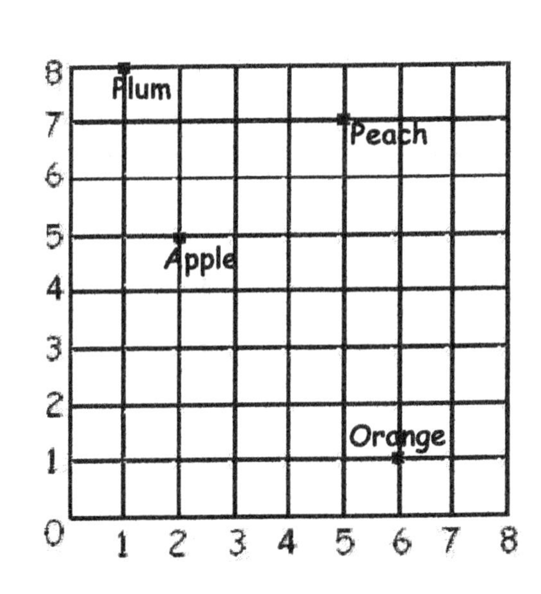

1.	2.	3.	4.
5.	6.	7.	8.
9.	10.	11.	12.
13.	14.	15.	16.
17.	18.	19.	20.

Lesson #64

1. Find the probability of rolling a number less than 6 on 1 roll of a die.

2. Write $\frac{75}{8}$ as a mixed number.

3. How many yards are in a mile?

4. Draw a right angle.

5. Marshall is 6 feet 4 inches tall. What is Marshall's height in inches?

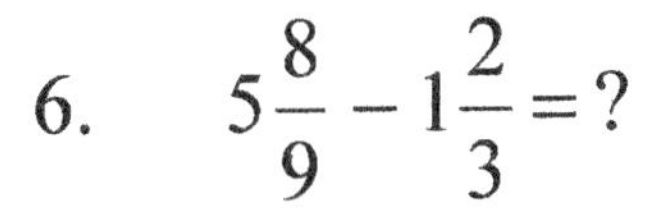

6. $5\frac{8}{9} - 1\frac{2}{3} = ?$

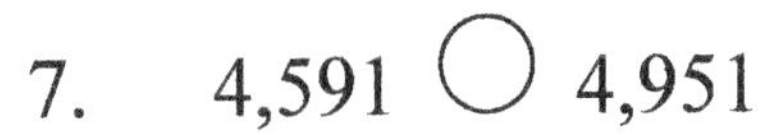

7. 4,591 ◯ 4,951

8. The Fahrenheit boiling temperature of water is __________.

9. $12{,}346 \div 6 = ?$

10. A closed figure made up of line segments is a(n) __________.

11. Which digit is in the millions place in 57,902,163?

12. $\frac{7}{8}$ ◯ $\frac{9}{11}$

13. Numbers that have only two factors are ____________ numbers.

14. $623 \times 7 = ?$

15. $12.7 + 27.9 = ?$

16. How many feet are in 6 yards?

17. $7{,}031 - 3{,}546 = ?$

18. $57 \times 41 = ?$

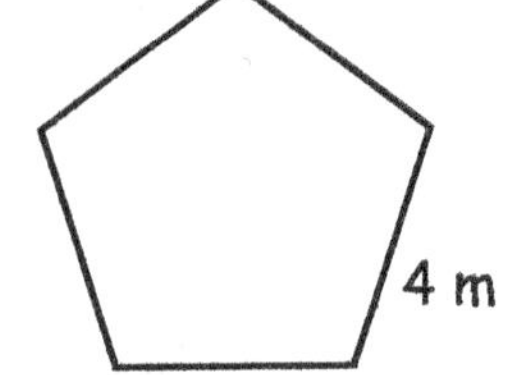

19. What is the perimeter of this regular pentagon?

20. Ali has 4 yards of string. Gayle has 200 inches of string. Who has more string? Explain how you found your answer.

1.	2.	3.	4.
5.	6.	7.	8.
9.	10.	11.	12.
13.	14.	15.	16.
17.	18.	19.	20.

Lesson #65

1. 461,218 + 381,356 = ?

2. Round 84,207,334 to the nearest hundred thousand.

3. $10\frac{1}{4} + 5\frac{2}{5} = ?$

4. How many feet are in 8 yards?

5. Find the area of a square whose sides measure 3 meters each.

6. Rewrite $\frac{12}{18}$ in simplest form.

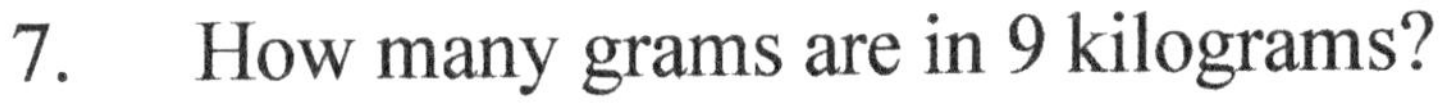

7. How many grams are in 9 kilograms?

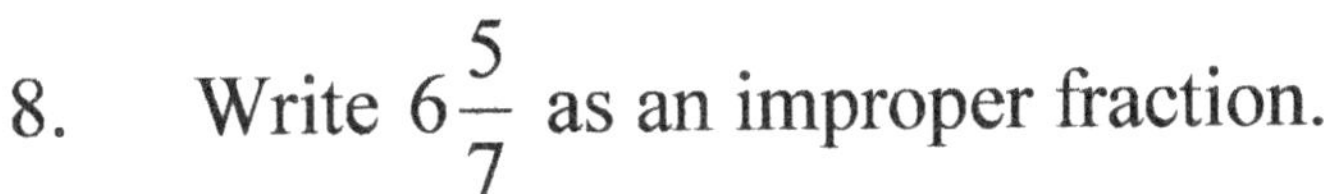

8. Write $6\frac{5}{7}$ as an improper fraction.

9. 75 + 18 + 35 = ?

10. 33 × 25 = ?

11. Make a factor tree for 60.

12. $\frac{6}{7} - \frac{1}{3} = ?$

13. Find the GCF of 25 and 30.

14. Draw a line segment.

15. 721 – 425 = ?

16. $\frac{8}{9} \bigcirc \frac{5}{6}$

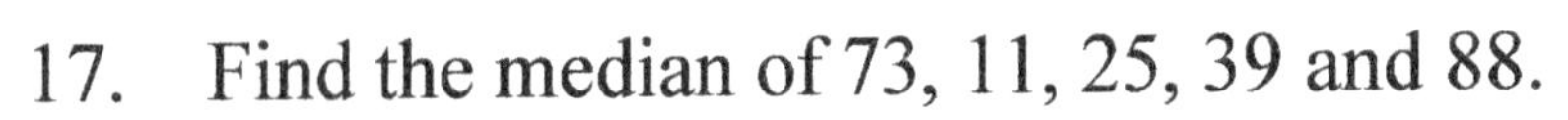

17. Find the median of 73, 11, 25, 39 and 88.

18. 420 ÷ 70 = ?

19. A quadrilateral has ____________ sides.

20. Forty people attended the play. 15 of the people were women, 10 were men and 15 were children. What fraction were men?

1.	2.	3.	4.
5.	6.	7.	8.
9.	10.	11.	12.
13.	14.	15.	16.
17.	18.	19.	20.

Lesson #66

1. $42{,}401 \times 3 = ?$

2. It is 1:40. What time will it be in 5 hours and 20 minutes?

3. How many gallons are 8 quarts?

4. $2\frac{1}{9} + 5\frac{1}{2} = ?$

5. Draw a right angle.

6. $\$83.42 - \$16.95 = ?$

7. Put $\frac{15}{25}$ in simplest form.

8. $53.94 + 16.8 = ?$

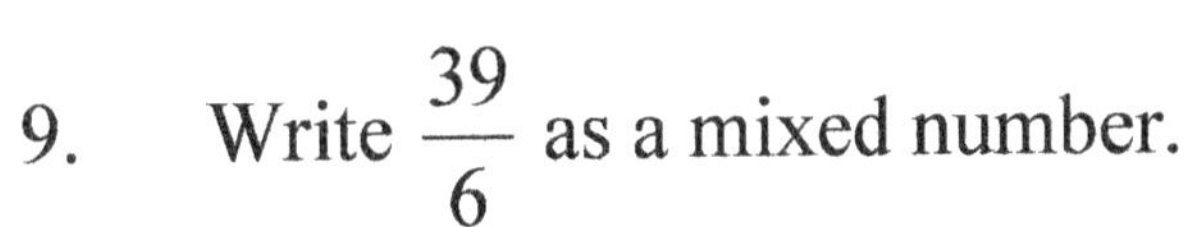

9. Write $\frac{39}{6}$ as a mixed number.

10. Which digit is in the hundred thousands place in 9,203,641?

11. $5{,}763 \div 3 = ?$

12. The answer to a subtraction problem is called the __________.

13. List the factors of 18.

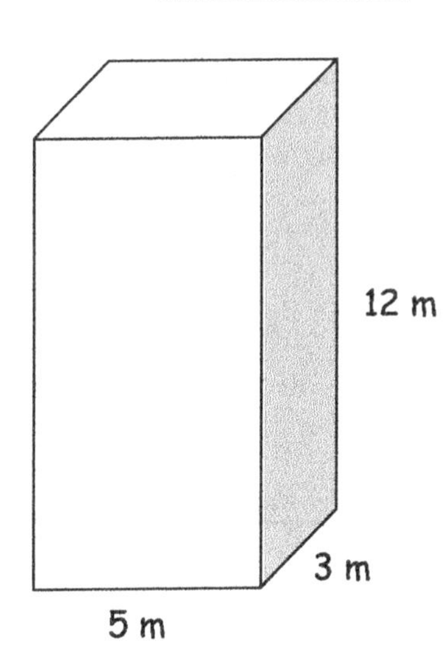

14. $\frac{7}{8} - \frac{1}{2} = ?$

15. Find the volume of the rectangular prism.

16. $147 \times 22 = ?$

17. Find the mode of 11, 29, 43, 29 and 29.

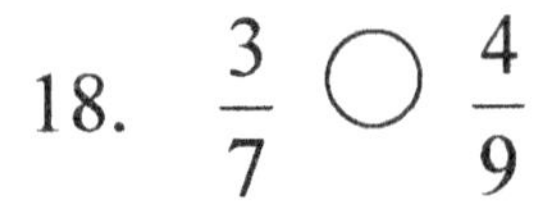

18. $\frac{3}{7} \bigcirc \frac{4}{9}$

19. How many feet are in 4 miles?

20. Rachel, Pedro, Mario, and Ling each have different-colored pencil cases. Mario's case is not red. Rachel's is not green or blue. Pedro's case is not blue. Ling's case is yellow. What color is each person's pencil case?

1.	2.	3.	4.
5.	6.	7.	8.
9.	10.	11.	12.
13.	14.	15.	16.
17.	18.	19.	20.

Lesson #67

1. How many minutes are in 3 hours?

2. What type of angle is shown?

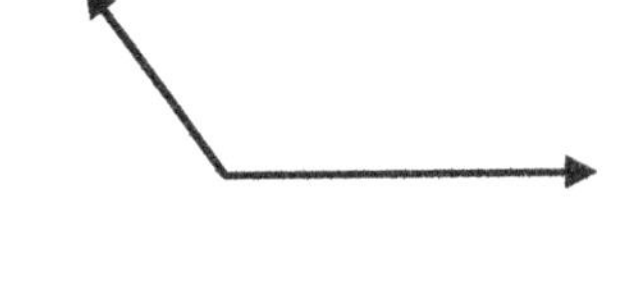

3. Write $\frac{51}{8}$ as a mixed number.

4. Which is the greater distance, 75 feet or 720 inches?

5. 7,416,294 + 8,729,304 = ?

6. $5\frac{2}{5} + 2\frac{1}{4} = ?$

7. Draw intersecting lines.

8. 60,000 – 37,315 = ?

9. Write 621,735 in expanded form.

10. $\frac{4}{9} = \frac{?}{72}$

11. On a Celsius thermometer, water boils at what temperature?

12. Write the formula for finding the perimeter of a regular polygon.

13. $77 \times 43 = ?$

14. What time was it 8 hours ago, if it is 4:00 now?

15. $30{,}405 \div 5 = ?$

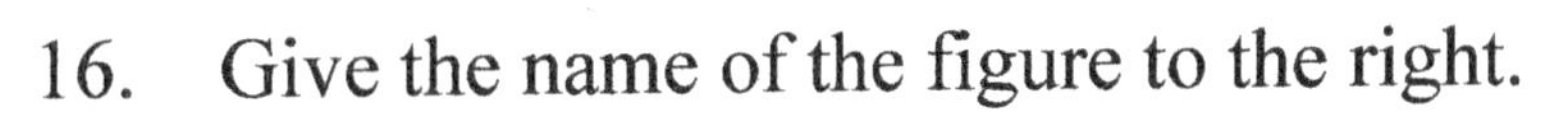

16. Give the name of the figure to the right.

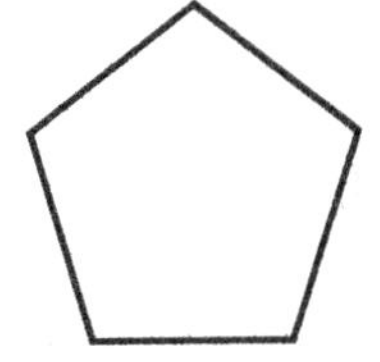

17. How many pounds are 112 ounces?

18. Find the radius of a circle whose diameter is 36 mm.

19. Find the LCM of 12 and 21.

20. Lamar had a coupon for candy at the video store. The original price of the candy was $3.75. Lamar paid only $1.85. What was the coupon worth?

1.	2.	3.	4.
5.	6.	7.	8.
9.	10.	11.	12.
13.	14.	15.	16.
17.	18.	19.	20.

Lesson #68

1. Make a factor tree for 16.
2. Reduce $\frac{16}{18}$ to simplest form.
3. Find the volume of a cube whose sides measure 5 inches.
4. Write the first 5 prime numbers.
5. $802 - 573 = ?$
6. $7\frac{2}{5} + 3\frac{1}{3} = ?$
7. $83 \times 31 = ?$
8. Draw a line.
9. $\frac{6}{7} - \frac{1}{3} = ?$
10. $361{,}247 + 285{,}932 = ?$

11. There are __________ degrees in a straight angle.
12. Write $7\frac{2}{3}$ as an improper fraction.
13. $890 \div 90 = ?$
14. Nine centuries are ________ years.
15. Round 986,345,219 to the nearest ten million.
16. Numbers with only 2 factors are __________ numbers.
17. Find the average of 450, 375 and 135.
18. Any number multiplied by zero has an answer of __________.
19. $2.05 - 0.47 = ?$
20. During the summer, the population of Copper Springs is 75,865. During the winter, the population drops to 16,473. How many more people visit Copper Springs in the summer than in the winter?

1.	2.	3.	4.
5.	6.	7.	8.
9.	10.	11.	12.
13.	14.	15.	16.
17.	18.	19.	20.

Lesson #69

1. Draw a hexagon.

2. 268,709 + 45,638 = ?

3. Find the GCF and the LCM of 12 and 18.

4. Find the perimeter of a pentagon whose sides measure 7 inches.

5. If it is 12:20 now, what time will it be in 7 hours and 10 minutes?

6. $540 \times 8 = ?$

7. $\frac{4}{9} \bigcirc \frac{5}{8}$

8. 9,021 – 4,589 = ?

9. How many inches are in a yard?

10. Is 53 a prime or a composite number?

11. Find the range and the median of 31, 77, 98, 10 and 59.

12. $875 \div 50 = ?$

13. How many quarts are in 10 gallons?

14. $13 \times 13 = ?$

15. What is the probability of rolling an even number on 1 roll of a die?

16. Mr. Harrison drove 22 miles on Monday, 44 miles on Tuesday, and 88 miles on Wednesday. If this pattern continues, how far will Mr. Harrison drive on Friday?

17. Round 346,752,091 to the nearest hundred million.

18. $13 - 9\frac{1}{8} = ?$

19. Draw an obtuse angle.

20. Figures with the same size and shape are ____________.

1.	2.	3.	4.
5.	6.	7.	8.
9.	10.	11.	12.
13.	14.	15.	16.
17.	18.	19.	20.

Lesson #70

1. $25{,}875 \times 4 = ?$

2. Write $\frac{9}{18}$ in simplest terms.

3. How many pounds are 5 tons?

4. $40{,}000 - 18{,}464 = ?$

5. $8\frac{1}{3} + 5\frac{3}{5} = ?$

6. $30.6 - 11.35 = ?$

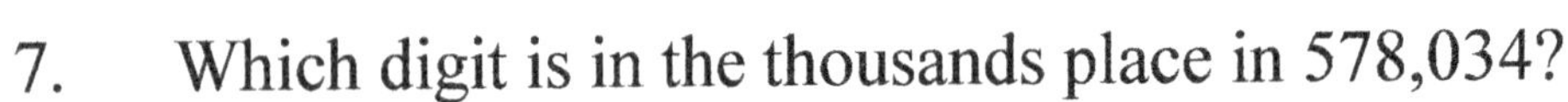

7. Which digit is in the thousands place in 578,034?

8. If it is 45 minutes after noon, what time is it?

9. Which is greater, 8,500 feet or 2 miles?

10. Draw perpendicular lines.

11. What is the area of this rectangle?

8 mm

15 mm

12. Draw two similar ovals.

13. $573 + 981 + 122 = ?$

14. $10 - 3\frac{3}{5} = ?$

15. How many degrees are in a right angle?

16. $32{,}848 \div 4 = ?$

17. The answer to an addition problem is called the ___________.

18. Estimate the product of 47 and 54.

19. Bobby jogged $2\frac{1}{2}$ miles on Friday and $3\frac{1}{8}$ miles on Saturday. How many miles did Bobby jog altogether?

20. How many faces does a cube have?

1.	2.	3.	4.
5.	6.	7.	8.
9.	10.	11.	12.
13.	14.	15.	16.
17.	18.	19.	20.

Lesson #71

1. How many cups are in 4 pints?
2. $65 \times 51 = ?$
3. Write the standard number for 50,000 + 9,000 + 800 + 2.
4. $614 - 385 = ?$
5. $15\frac{1}{6} - 8\frac{5}{6} = ?$
6. Classify the angle by type.

7. The bottom number in a fraction is the _________.
8. Draw a ray.
9. $378{,}503 + 251{,}764 = ?$
10. $784 \div 24 = ?$
11. $6\frac{2}{3} + 4\frac{1}{4} = ?$
12. $67 + \_\_\_\_ = 91$

13. How many millimeters are in 4 meters?
14. If the diameter of a circle is 36 inches, what is the radius?
15. Change $\frac{7}{28}$ to simplest form.
16. Joey's karate class begins at 7:00 p.m. It takes him 8 minutes to walk to the bus stop and 22 minutes for the bus ride. After getting off of the bus, he walks 5 minutes to the class. What time should he leave his house if he wants to get to class on time?
17. $\frac{5}{6} = \frac{40}{?}$
18. Which number is in the millions place in 357,098,216?
19. What is the shape of a can of corn?
20. Nine weeks are how many days?

1.	2.	3.	4.
5.	6.	7.	8.
9.	10.	11.	12.
13.	14.	15.	16.
17.	18.	19.	20.

Lesson #72

1. How many teaspoons are in 7 tablespoons?

2. Write $\frac{49}{8}$ as a mixed number.

3. $345 \div 25 = ?$

4. Find the area of the square.

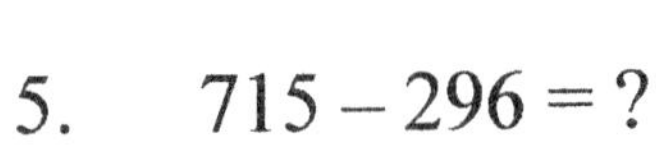

5. $715 - 296 = ?$

6. Two figures having the same shape, but different size are ________.

7. On the Fahrenheit temperature scale, water freezes at ___________.

8. What time was it 5 hours and 5 minutes ago, if it is 3:15 now?

9. Which digit is in the thousands place in 6,348,129?

10. Find the LCM of 9 and 15.

11. $4\frac{2}{5} + 8\frac{2}{3} = ?$

12. $16 - 8\frac{4}{9} = ?$

13. $69 + 55 + 73 = ?$

14. How many degrees are in a straight angle?

15. Find the mode of 54, 60, 29, 54 and 69.

16. Make a factor tree for 64.

17. Five hundred years is _________ centuries.

18. $94 \times 32 = ?$

19. List the factors of 24.

20. For decorating the gym, Jackie has a ribbon that is 14.6 feet long and Rosie has a ribbon that is 10.8 feet long. How much longer is Jackie's ribbon?

1.	2.	3.	4.
5.	6.	7.	8.
9.	10.	11.	12.
13.	14.	15.	16.
17.	18.	19.	

Lesson #73

1. $347 + 625 = ?$
2. Which factors of 12 are also factors of 24?
3. Find the LCM of 16 and 18.
4. Draw 2 similar triangles.
5. Write $\frac{16}{24}$ in simplest form.
6. $\frac{7}{8} = \frac{21}{?}$
7. $16.7 + 35.4 = ?$
8. $12 - 6\frac{4}{7} = ?$
9. What do you call the middle number in a set of numbers?
10. Write $\frac{34}{5}$ as a mixed number.
11. How many nickels are in $4?
12. How many inches are in 5 feet?
13. What is the name of this figure?

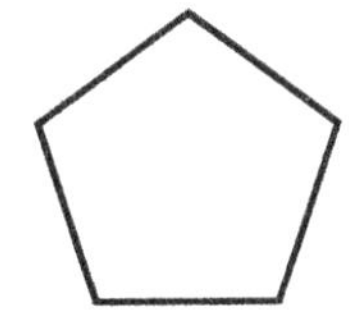

14. Rename $9\frac{1}{4}$ as an improper fraction.
15. $\frac{8}{9} \bigcirc \frac{9}{11}$
16. $7\frac{1}{3} + 2\frac{1}{4} = ?$
17. Give the length of the segment in inches.

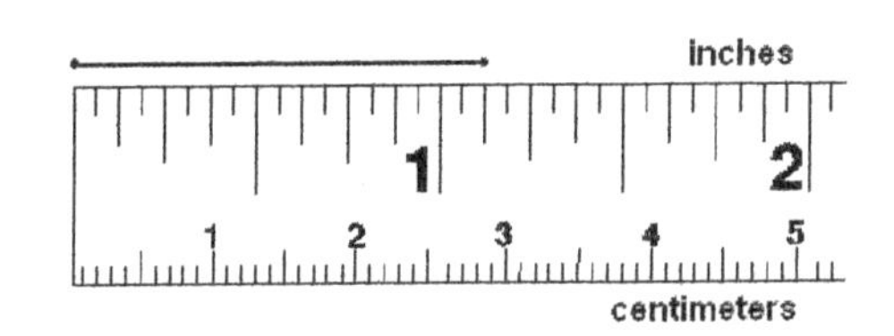

18. $500 \times 80 = ?$
19. Round 45,708,962 to the nearest ten million.
20. The Barrett family spent $6.25 each for 2 adult movie tickets and $4.75 each for 4 children's tickets. They spent $22.50 on snacks. How much change did they receive from $100?

1.	2.	3.	4.
5.	6.	7.	8.
9.	10.	11.	12.
13.	14.	15.	16.
17.	18.	19.	20.

Lesson #74

1. $573 \times 6 = ?$
2. Find the GCF of 10 and 12.
3. $5\frac{2}{5} + 4\frac{2}{3} = ?$
4. $7{,}000 - 3{,}645 = ?$
5. $15\frac{1}{2} - 10\frac{3}{5} = ?$
6. $73{,}485 + 22{,}386 = ?$
7. Draw perpendicular lines.
8. $\$50.00 - \$26.75 = ?$

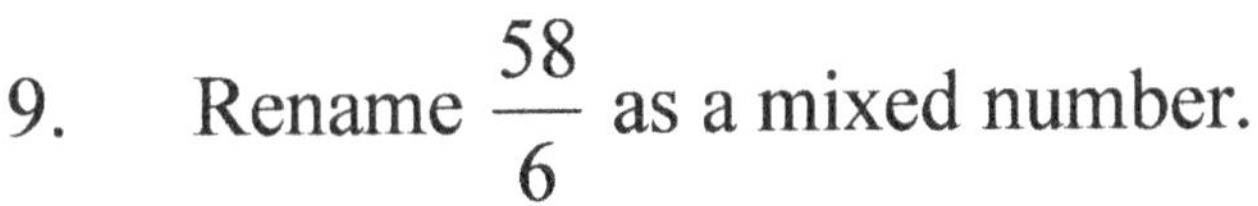

9. Rename $\frac{58}{6}$ as a mixed number.

10. Find the range of 155, 88, 69, 100 and 31.
11. How many sides does an octagon have?
12. What do you call the number that occurs most often in a set of numbers?
13. Find the average of 36, 113, 29, 18 and 54.
14. $6{,}000 \times 4 = ?$
15. $785 \div 5 = ?$
16. What is the area of the rectangle?

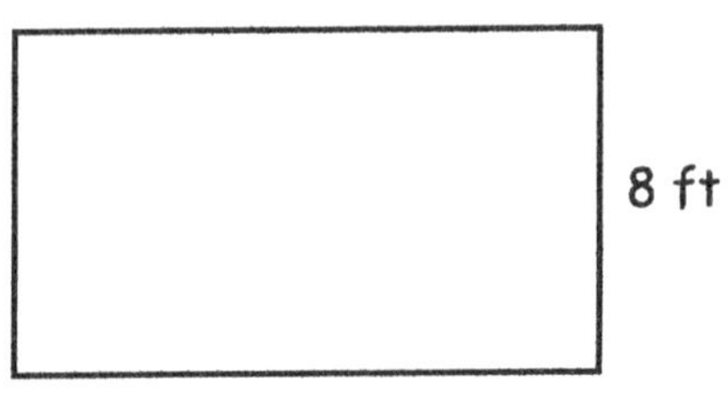

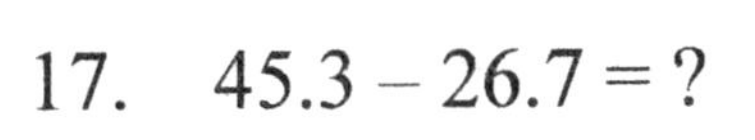

17. $45.3 - 26.7 = ?$
18. Which is greater, 6 quarts or 10 pints?
19. Grandma made an afghan that was $48\frac{1}{2}$ inches long. She added $1\frac{3}{4}$ inches of fringe along the edges. How long is her afghan now?
20. $\frac{6}{7} \bigcirc \frac{2}{3}$

1.	2.	3.	4.
5.	6.	7.	8.
9.	10.	11.	12.
13.	14.	15.	16.
17.	18.	19.	20.

Lesson #75

1. How many milliliters are in a liter?
2. $969 \div 6 = ?$
3. Round 719,485 to the nearest hundred thousand.
4. Find the LCM of 12 and 15.
5. Find the perimeter of this figure.

16 in

6. Rename $5\frac{2}{3}$ as an improper fraction.
7. $\frac{5}{6} = \frac{?}{42}$
8. The answer to a division problem is the _________.
9. $22 \times 56 = ?$
10. Is 42 a prime or a composite number?
11. In $\frac{7}{8}$, which number is the denominator?
12. List the factors of 36.
13. On the Celsius scale, water freezes at ___________.
14. Kendra is 4 feet 8 inches tall. What is her height in inches?
15. $23\frac{1}{4} + 16\frac{1}{3} = ?$
16. $(3 \times 4) + 15 = ?$
17. Put $\frac{12}{24}$ in simplest form.

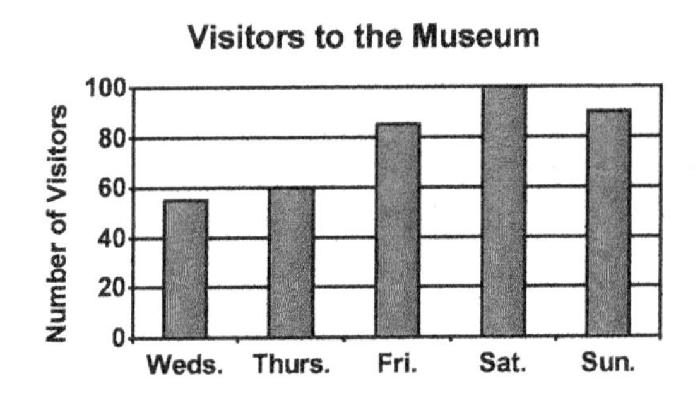

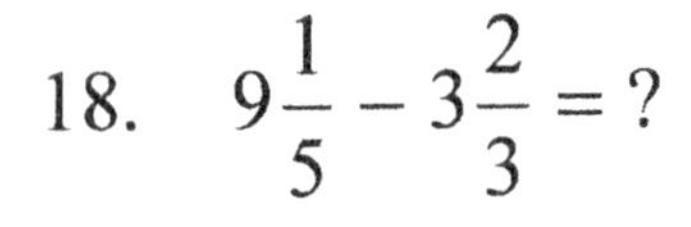

18. $9\frac{1}{5} - 3\frac{2}{3} = ?$
19. How many more people came on Saturday than on Wednesday?
20. What was the average number of visitors per day?

1.	2.	3.	4.
5.	6.	7.	8.
9.	10.	11.	12.
13.	14.	15.	16.
17.	18.	19.	20.

Lesson #76

1. $500 - 156 = ?$
2. On a Fahrenheit thermometer, water freezes at ____________.
3. Write $\frac{10}{15}$ in simplest terms.

4. Find the perimeter of the pentagon.

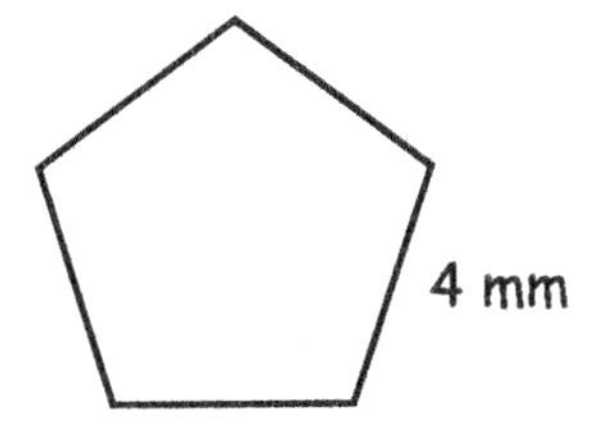

5. How many pounds are in 6 tons?

6. $10 - 5\frac{2}{5} = ?$
7. $96 + 33 + 72 = ?$
8. $63 \times 34 = ?$
9. Draw a ray.

10. Find the GCF of 12 and 18.
11. $8\frac{1}{2} + 9\frac{1}{3} = ?$
12. The answer to an addition problem is called the ____________.
13. Which digit is in the ten thousands place in 125,607,893?
14. Draw a hexagon. How many sides does it have?
15. $850 \div 50 = ?$
16. Identify the name of the figure shown to the right.

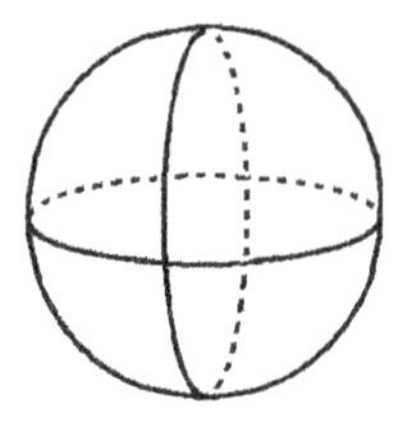

17. $33.81 + 16.9 = ?$
18. Write the next three numbers in the sequence. 157, 164, 171, ...
19. In the morning the temperature was 32°F. By 4:00 p.m. the thermometer read 63°F. What was the change in temperature from morning to afternoon?
20. Change $6\frac{4}{5}$ to an improper fraction.

1.	2.	3.	4.
5.	6.	7.	8.
9.	10.	11.	12.
13.	14.	15.	16.
17.	18.	19.	20.

Lesson #77

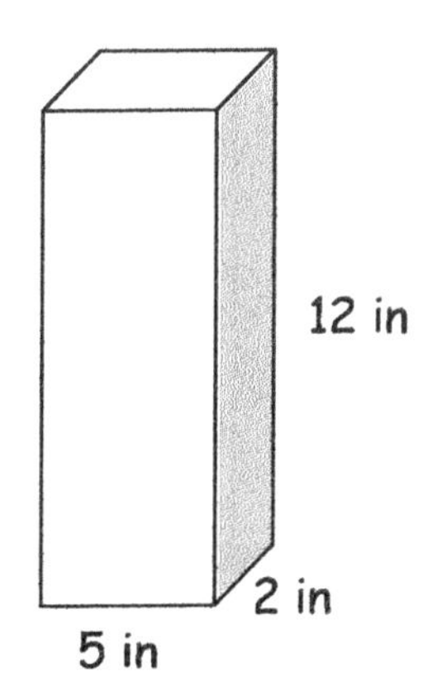

1. Is the number 28 prime or composite?
2. Draw intersecting lines.
3. Find the volume of the prism.
4. How many quarters are in $10?
5. $65 \times 20 = ?$

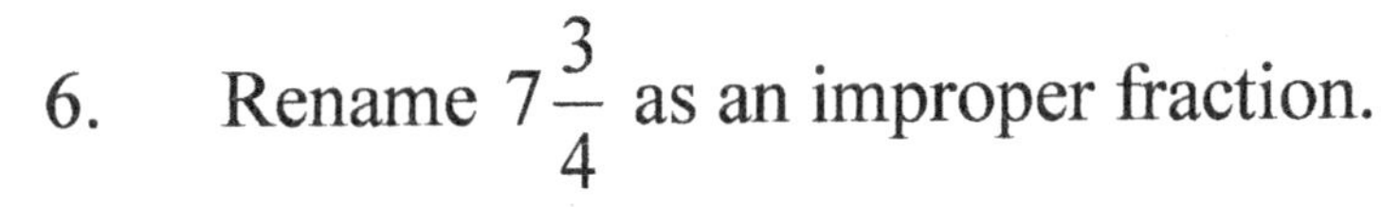

6. Rename $7\frac{3}{4}$ as an improper fraction.
7. $\frac{5}{6} + \frac{2}{3} = ?$
8. $751 + 174 + 332 = ?$
9. $8.2 - 4.78 = ?$
10. How many inches are in 4 feet?
11. $9\frac{1}{10} - 4\frac{2}{5} = ?$
12. Find the LCM of 5, 6 and 10.
13. $25{,}600 - 15{,}475 = ?$
14. Which is greater, 5 gallons or 16 quarts?

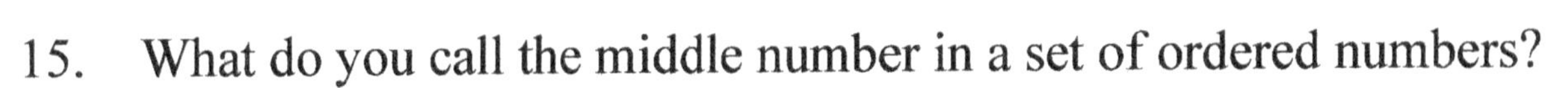

15. What do you call the middle number in a set of ordered numbers?
16. How many sides does a quadrilateral have?
17. $\frac{7}{8} \bigcirc \frac{5}{6}$
18. It is 6:20. What time will it be in 4 hours and 10 minutes?

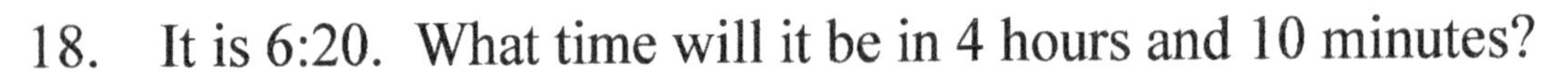

19. Hannah poured 4 pints of liquid into the 5 quart punch bowl. How many more quarts should Hannah add to fill the bowl?
20. $26{,}785 \div 3 = ?$

1.	2.	3.	4.
5.	6.	7.	8.
9.	10.	11.	12.
13.	14.	15.	16.
17.	18.	19.	20.

Lesson #78

1. Closed shapes made up of line segments are _______________.
2. Draw an acute angle.
3. The figure shown is a parallelogram. Draw one.
4. $(40 + 5) \div 9 = ?$

5. Draw parallel vertical lines.
6. Round 874 to the nearest ten.
7. $5\frac{1}{4} - 3\frac{3}{4} = ?$
8. $9.21 + 3.46 = ?$
9. $732 \times 7 = ?$
10. $4,000 - 1,461 = ?$
11. How many months are there between December 5th and June 5th ?
12. Which factors of 18 are also factors of 24?
13. List the next three numbers in the sequence. 5,300 5,400 5,500 ...
14. Draw a rectangle. Label the length 12 mm and the width 6 mm Find the area of the rectangle.
15. $8\frac{2}{3} + 4\frac{1}{5} = ?$

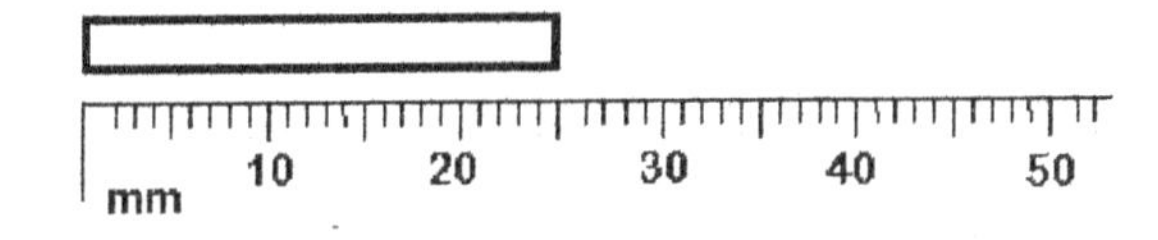

16. $3,175 \div 5 = ?$
17. Give the length of the rectangle in millimeters.
18. What year is 2 decades before 1972?
19. Debbie added $2\frac{1}{2}$ cups of flour to her batter. Melissa added another $1\frac{3}{4}$ cups of flour. How much flour is in the batter?
20. A number with more than two factors is a _______ number.

1.	2.	3.	4.
5.	6.	7.	8.
9.	10.	11.	12.
13.	14.	15.	16.
17.	18.	19.	20.

Lesson #79

1. $7 - 2\frac{1}{2} = ?$
2. Round 4,851,369 to the nearest thousand.
3. $66 + 25 + 17 + 31 = ?$

4. $80{,}000 - 36{,}528 = ?$
5. How many ounces are in 7 pounds?
6. $91 \times 45 = ?$
7. Change $\frac{7}{2}$ to a mixed number.
8. Find the range of 61, 13, 55, 83 and 121.
9. $4{,}480 \div 40 = ?$

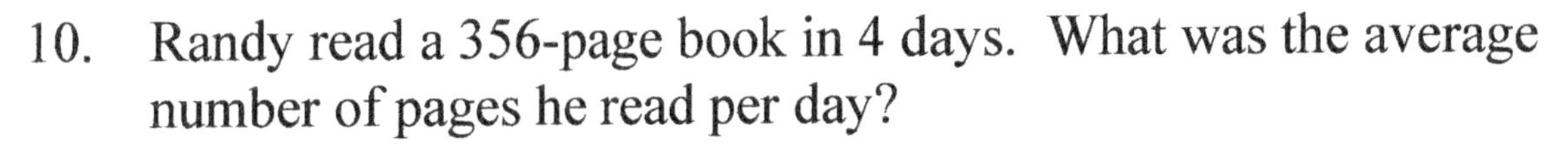

10. Randy read a 356-page book in 4 days. What was the average number of pages he read per day?
11. Change $5\frac{3}{5}$ to an improper fraction.
12. If you sleep 6 hours a day, what fraction of the day do you sleep?
13. $\frac{3}{8} = \frac{?}{16}$
14. Write the next three numbers in the sequence. 261, 256, 251, ...
15. If a semi can carry $4\frac{1}{2}$ tons, how many pounds can it carry?
16. $4.2 + 2.5 + 1.7 = ?$
17. Write the name of this shape.

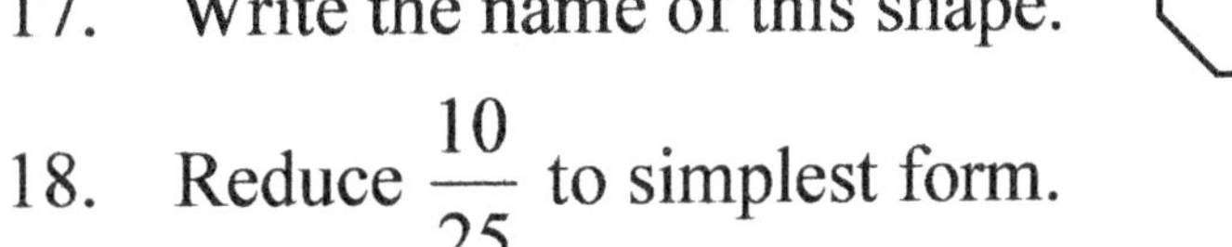

18. Reduce $\frac{10}{25}$ to simplest form.
19. If a kitten weighs half of a pound, how many ounces does it weigh?
20. $5\frac{1}{4} + 5\frac{2}{5} = ?$

1.	2.	3.	4.
5.	6.	7.	8.
9.	10.	11.	12.
13.	14.	15.	16.
17.	18.	19.	20.

Lesson #80

1. List the factors of 18.
2. Draw a line segment.
3. Are these figures similar or congruent? 
4. Give the definition of *mode*.
5. $9{,}020 - 4{,}365 = ?$

6. $924 \times 3 = ?$
7. $\$46.99 + \$32.56 = ?$
8. How many milliliters are in a liter?
9. List the first 5 prime numbers.
10. $\frac{7}{8} + \frac{1}{8} = ?$
11. How many cups are in a pint?
12. $6\frac{2}{5} - 2\frac{4}{5} = ?$

13. Find the GCF of 10 and 25.

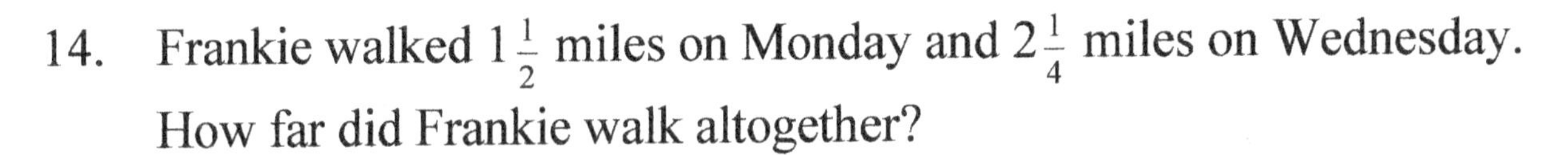

14. Frankie walked $1\frac{1}{2}$ miles on Monday and $2\frac{1}{4}$ miles on Wednesday. How far did Frankie walk altogether?
15. At 90 minutes after noon, what time is it?
16. $9{,}052 \div 45 = ?$
17. $\frac{6}{7} \bigcirc \frac{9}{10}$
18. Draw a square. Show 2 lines of symmetry.
19. Write the formula for finding the volume of a prism.
20. Rewrite $\frac{9}{12}$ in simplest terms.

1.	2.	3.	4.
5.	6.	7.	8.
9.	10.	11.	12.
13.	14.	15.	16.
17.	18.	19.	20.

Lesson #81

1. Is 31 a prime or a composite number?
2. Draw an obtuse angle.
3. 892 + 566 = ?
4. Round 45,276,362 to the nearest ten million.
5. The diameter of a circle is 30 mm. What is its radius?
6. How many inches are in 9 feet?
7. Which is the greater distance, 7 yards or 20 feet?
8. Find the average and the median of 18, 25, 15, 29 and 18.
9. The 1st show at the Science Museum starts at 12:15. If there is a show every 2 hours and 15 minutes. At what time is the 4th show?
10. $8\frac{1}{3} - 3\frac{2}{3} = ?$
11. Find the LCM of 9 and 21.
12. 50,000 – 32,571 = ?
13. $5\frac{2}{5} + 7\frac{2}{3} = ?$
14. 975 ÷ 25 = ?
15. $\frac{8}{11}$ ○ $\frac{7}{12}$

16. At what temperature does water boil on the Fahrenheit scale?
17. A closed figure made up of line segments is called a(n) __________.
18. Put these numbers in order from greatest to least.
    7,652 7,498 7,948 7,562
19. Rename $12\frac{1}{2}$ as an improper fraction.
20. $70 \times 80 = ?$

1.	2.	3.	4.
5.	6.	7.	8.
9.	10.	11.	12.
13.	14.	15.	16.
17.	18.	19.	20.

Lesson #82

1. Find the GCF of 18 and 24.

2. $68 + \_\_\_\_ = 125$

3. Write the name of the shape.

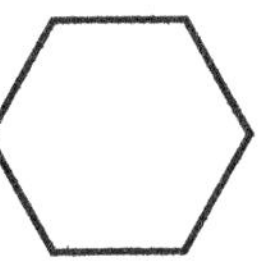

4. $32 \times 14 = ?$

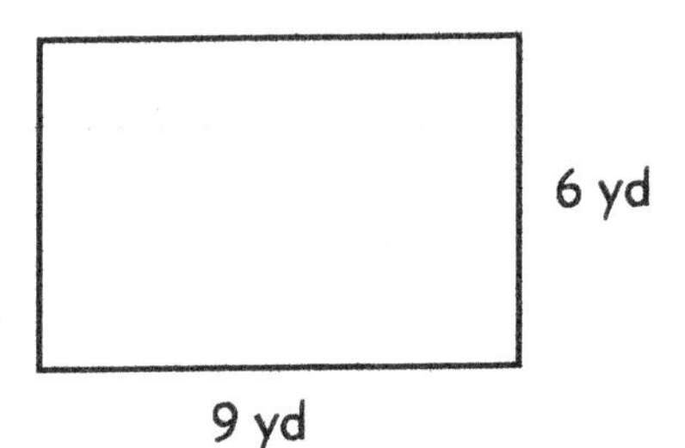

5. How many days are in 14 weeks?

6. Find the perimeter and the area of the rectangle.

7. $19{,}465 + 24{,}582 = ?$

8. Write $\frac{14}{21}$ in simplest form.

9. What is the probability that the spinner will land in area C?

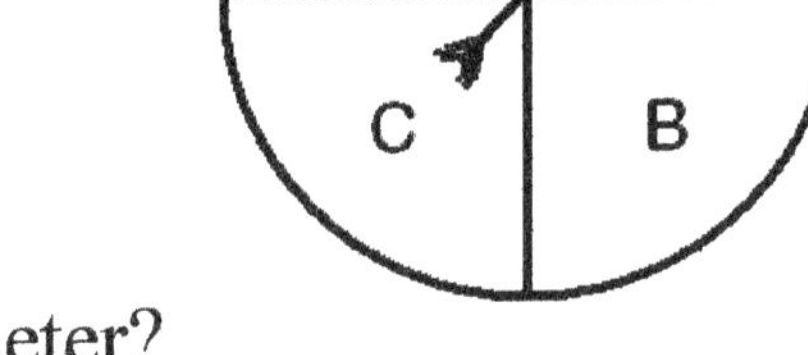

10. How many quarts are in 9 gallons?

11. Write $\frac{85}{9}$ as a mixed number.

12. What is the average of 420, 139, 275 and 398?

13. The radius of a circle is 16 m. What is its diameter?

14. $\frac{4}{7} \bigcirc \frac{11}{12}$

15. Find the median of 68, 71, 87, 50 and 23.

16. $\frac{2}{5} \times \frac{1}{3} = ?$

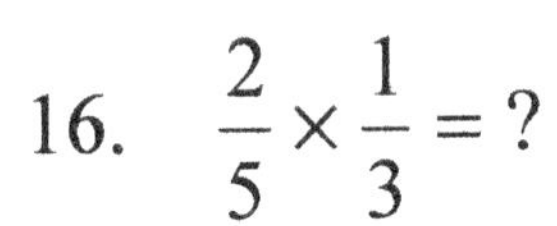

17. $11\frac{1}{5} - 6\frac{3}{10} = ?$

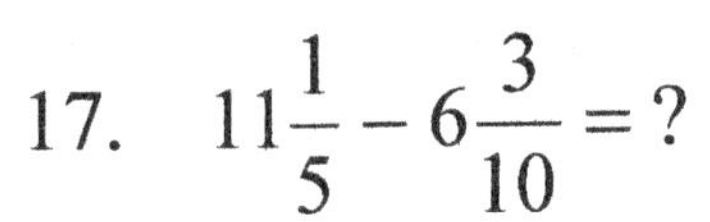

18. $750 \div 30 = ?$

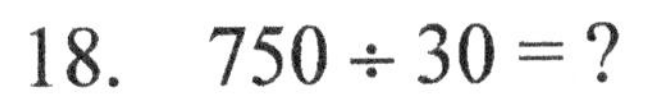

19. Figures having the same shape, but different size are ________.

20. Aunt Cindy is making trail mix. Her recipe calls for $3\frac{1}{4}$ cups of pretzels and $1\frac{2}{5}$ cups of nuts. How much trail mix will this make?

1.	2.	3.	4.
5.	6.	7.	8.
9.	10.	11.	12.
13.	14.	15.	16.
17.	18.	19.	20.

Lesson #83

1. Round 26,875 to the nearest thousand.
2. $82.5 + 39.86 = ?$
3. How many cups are in 5 pints?
4. $62 \times 41 = ?$
5. Rename $\frac{75}{9}$ as a mixed number.
6. Is 13 a prime or a composite number?
7. $(30 \times 5) \times 3 = ?$
8. Find the median of 11, 76, 19, 33 and 95.
9. How many days are in 15 weeks?
10. $6\frac{5}{8} - 1\frac{1}{4} = ?$

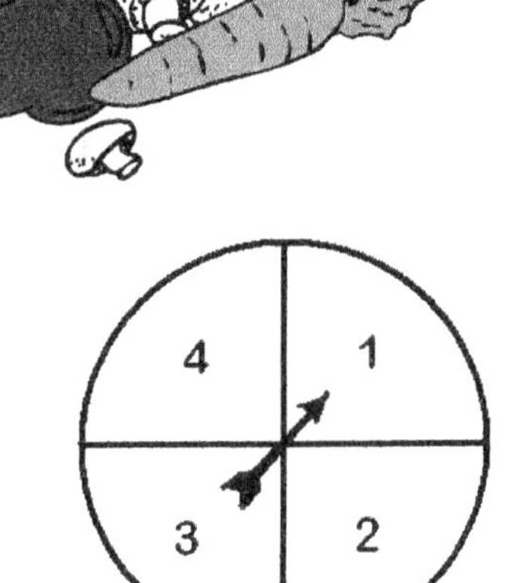

11. What is the probability that the spinner will stop on each?
    a) an even number b) a number less than 5
12. How many centimeters are in 10 meters?
13. Draw a right angle.
14. Is there a line of symmetry shown on the figure?

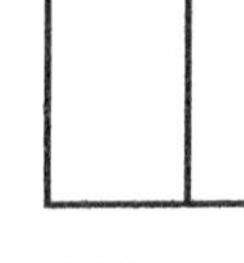

15. $7{,}560 \div 4 = ?$
16. Find the volume of the prism.

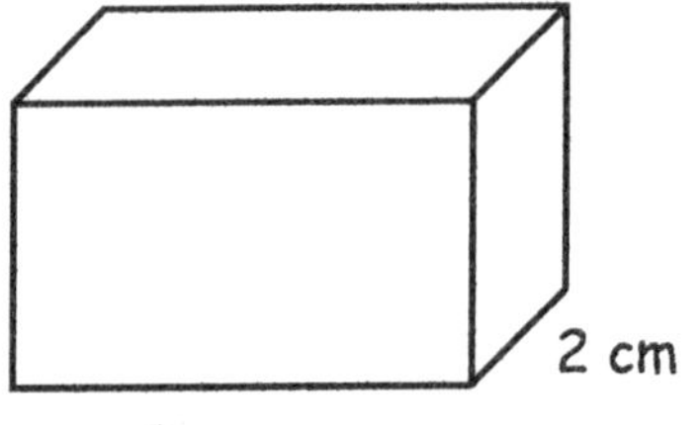

17. Find the LCM of 15 and 25.
18. On the Celsius temperature scale, water boils at ___________.
19. My doctor told me that $\frac{1}{4}$ of the foods I eat should be vegetables and $\frac{1}{5}$ should be whole grains. What fraction of the foods I eat should be vegetables or whole grains?
20. $\frac{4}{5} \times \frac{10}{16} = ?$

1.	2.	3.	4.
5.	6.	7.	8.
9.	10.	11.	12.
13.	14.	15.	16.
17.	18.	19.	20.

Lesson #84

1. $645 + 77 + 6 = ?$

2. Make a factor tree for 70.

3. Write $\frac{15}{25}$ in simplest form.

4. $205 \times 14 = ?$

5. Find the LCM of 6, 10 and 12.

6. $9.4 - 3.76 = ?$

7. $6\frac{2}{3} + 7\frac{1}{6} = ?$

8. $\frac{7}{9} \bigcirc \frac{4}{5}$

9. $802 - 183 = ?$

10. If it is 10:25 now, what time was it 3 hours and 10 minutes ago?

11. How many centuries are 600 years?

12. Find the median of 94, 27, 10, 88 and 53.

13. $15 - 9\frac{2}{9} = ?$

14. Rich is 6 feet 7 inches tall. How many inches tall is Rich?

15. Round 523,780 to the nearest ten thousand.

16. $\frac{2}{3} \times \frac{9}{10} = ?$

17. Write the formula for finding the volume of a prism.

18. How many pounds are in 5 tons?

19. On a Celsius thermometer, water freezes at ___________.

20. Carrie mixed $\frac{1}{2}$ cup of cashews and $\frac{3}{4}$ cup of almonds. How many cups of nuts did she have?

1.	2.	3.	4.
5.	6.	7.	8.
9.	10.	11.	12.
13.	14.	15.	16.
17.	18.	19.	20.

Lesson #85

1. $663 + 278 = ?$

2. $3\frac{1}{4} + 9\frac{2}{5} = ?$

3. Find the GCF of 16 and 24.

4. $\frac{3}{4} \times \frac{2}{9} = ?$

5. Write the formula for finding the area of a quadrilateral.

6. $\frac{5}{7} = \frac{?}{42}$

7. A theatre has 165 seats arranged in 11 rows, with the same number of seats in each row. How many seats are in each row?

8. Which is greater, 144 ounces or 7 pounds?

9. $9\frac{1}{3} - 4\frac{2}{3} = ?$

10. How many feet are in a mile?

11. $908 - 555 = ?$

12. Find the average of 87, 42 and 90.

13. Change $\frac{49}{6}$ to a mixed number.

14. $300 \times 600 = ?$

15. Draw a pentagon. Draw a line of symmetry through it.

16. Round 136,856,715 to the nearest ten million.

17. Find the mode of 56, 21, 12, 46 and 21.

18. Is the fraction $\frac{8}{12}$ in simplest form?

19. Figures with the same size and shape are called _______ shapes.

20. Sharon worked $3\frac{3}{4}$ hours on Tuesday and $6\frac{1}{2}$ hours on Wednesday. How many hours did she work in all?

1.	2.	3.	4.
5.	6.	7.	8.
9.	10.	11.	12.
13.	14.	15.	16.
17.	18.	19.	20.

Lesson #86

1. How many ounces are in a pound?

2. $12.6 - 9.74 = ?$

3. Reduce $\frac{16}{18}$ to simplest terms.

4. Find the GCF and the LCM of 16 and 24.

5. Draw a pentagon. Label a side 9 inches long. Find the perimeter.

6. $31{,}854 + 19{,}728 = ?$

7. Which digit is in the millions place in 216,098,543?

8. Figures having the same shape, but different size are ___________.

9. $\frac{5}{6} \times \frac{12}{25} = ?$

10. $23\frac{1}{5} + 17\frac{1}{4} = ?$

11. $40{,}000 - 27{,}367 = ?$

12. How many years are 3 decades?

13. Draw an obtuse angle.

14. $855 \div 32 = ?$

15. Round 54,675,213 to the nearest hundred thousand.

16. Water boils at ___________ degrees Fahrenheit.

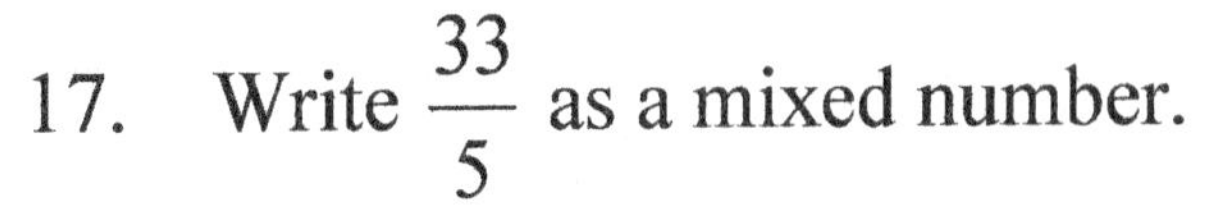

17. Write $\frac{33}{5}$ as a mixed number.

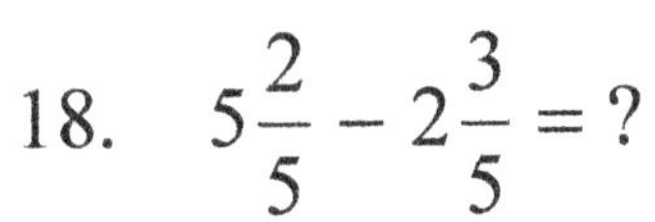

18. $5\frac{2}{5} - 2\frac{3}{5} = ?$

19. What is the most popular dog breed?

20. How many children chose either a Golden Retriever or a Great Dane?

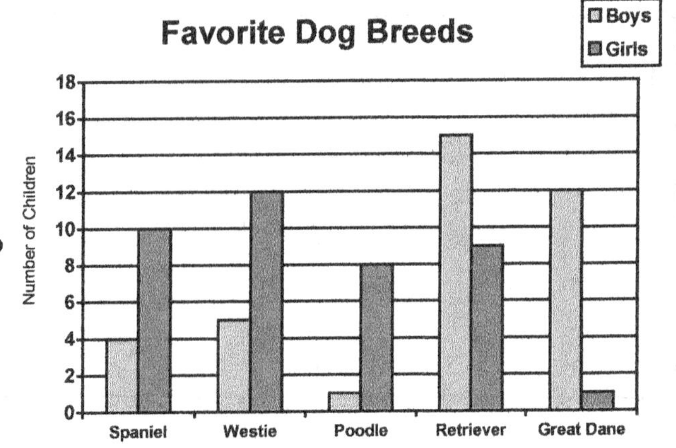

1.	2.	3.	4.
5.	6.	7.	8.
9.	10.	11.	12.
13.	14.	15.	16.
17.	18.	19.	20.

Lesson #87

1. Is 72 a prime or a composite number?
2. $\frac{3}{7} \times \frac{14}{15} = ?$
3. How many centimeters are in 9 meters?
4. Find the LCM of 12 and 15.
5. List the factors of 24.
6. $10\frac{1}{5} - 3\frac{4}{5} = ?$

7. Which is greater, 300 minutes or $2\frac{1}{2}$ hours?

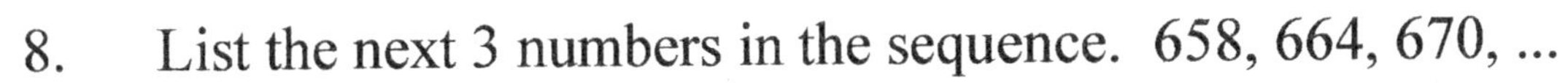

8. List the next 3 numbers in the sequence. 658, 664, 670, ...
9. $\frac{6}{7} \bigcirc \frac{5}{6}$

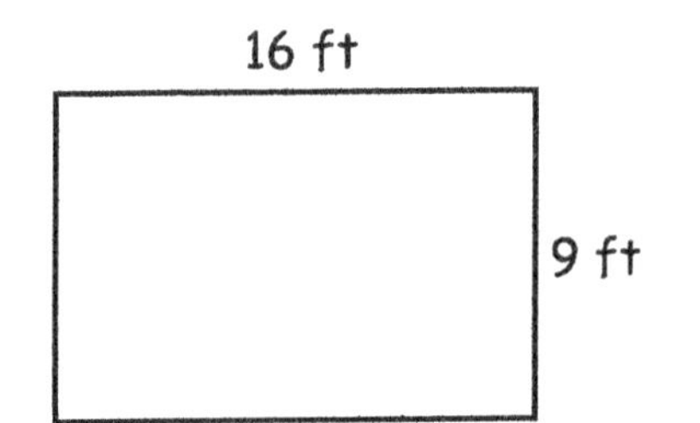

10. Find the area of the rectangle.
11. $31\frac{1}{2} + 16\frac{2}{5} = ?$
12. The diameter of a circle is 50 in. What is the radius?
13. $60 \times 47 = ?$
14. Draw a parallelogram.
15. Round 58,967 to the nearest ten.
16. $2{,}678 \div 4 = ?$

17. Change $7\frac{1}{3}$ to an improper fraction.
18. How many pounds are in $6\frac{1}{2}$ tons?

19. Draw perpendicular lines.
20. Mitchell bought a small pizza for $6.99, a bag of chips for $1.85, and a can of soda for $0.89. What was his change from a $10 bill?

1.	2.	3.	4.
5.	6.	7.	8.
9.	10.	11.	12.
13.	14.	15.	16.
17.	18.	19.	20.

Lesson #88

1. $\frac{5}{6} \times \frac{12}{15} = ?$

2. $1\frac{3}{5} + 6\frac{2}{5} = ?$

3. Draw intersecting lines.

4. Vicki ate 15 cookies last week. If she ate 5 cookies Friday, what fraction of the week's cookies did she eat Friday? What fraction of the cookies did she eat during the rest of the week?

5. $600 - 185 = ?$

6. A quadrilateral has _______ sides.

7. $465 + 276 + 318 = ?$

8. $8\frac{1}{6} - 2\frac{5}{6} = ?$

9. How many inches are in a yard?

10. $16.7 + 24.85 = ?$

11. $71 \times 42 = ?$

12. List the factors of 18.

13. $7\frac{2}{3} + 3\frac{1}{6} = ?$

14. Draw a ray.

15. An eight-sided shape is a(n) _____________.

16. What is the number that occurs most often in a set of numbers?

17. How many degrees are in a straight angle?

18. $575 \div 25 = ?$

19. Write $\frac{19}{4}$ as a mixed number.

20. Explain how to find the average of a set of numbers.

1.	2.	3.	4.
5.	6.	7.	8.
9.	10.	11.	12.
13.	14.	15.	16.
17.	18.	19.	20.

Lesson #89

1. Write $8\frac{4}{5}$ as an improper fraction.
2. $15.3 - 9.65 = ?$
3. Draw 2 similar rectangles.
4. $622 \times 9 = ?$
5. Rewrite $\frac{12}{16}$ in simplest form.
6. How many days are in 8 weeks?
7. $984 + 473 + 221 = ?$
8. $\frac{5}{9} = \frac{?}{36}$
9. Find the perimeter and the area of a square if a side measures 12 in.
10. $5{,}000 - 2{,}873 = ?$
11. It is 2:30. What time was it 3 hours and 30 minutes ago?
12. List the factors of 12.
13. Find the GCF of 16 and 24.
14. $1{,}245 \div 3 = ?$
15. Shawna ran 420 yards in 3 minutes. At this rate, how many yards can she run in 6 minutes?
16. $3 \times \frac{1}{6} = ?$
17. Draw an obtuse angle.
18. How many dimes are in $4?
19. Derrick had 20 trophies and $\frac{1}{4}$ of them were golf trophies. How many trophies were not for golf?
20. Any number multiplied by zero has a product of ___________.

1.	2.	3.	4.
5.	6.	7.	8.
9.	10.	11.	12.
13.	14.	15.	16.
17.	18.	19.	20.

Lesson #90

1. Draw a line segment.

2. Which is greater, 10 quarters or 20 dimes?

3. $83 \times 12 = ?$

4. Is 43 a prime number or a composite number?

5. Find the mode of 146, 99, 65, 21 and 99.

6. $35.1 - 23.78 = ?$

7. $18\frac{2}{7} - 12\frac{5}{7} = ?$

8. $\frac{5}{6} \bigcirc \frac{2}{3}$

9. $\frac{8}{16} \times \frac{12}{14} = ?$

10. Make a factor tree for 32.

11. $76{,}908 + 34{,}775 = ?$

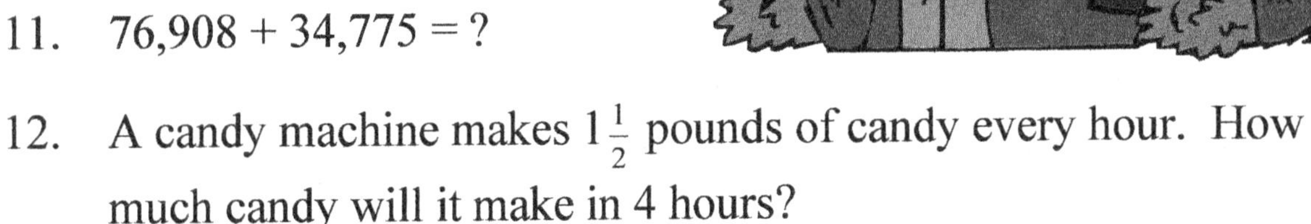

12. A candy machine makes $1\frac{1}{2}$ pounds of candy every hour. How much candy will it make in 4 hours?

13. $(600 + 400) \div 20 = ?$

14. Find the volume of the rectangular prism.

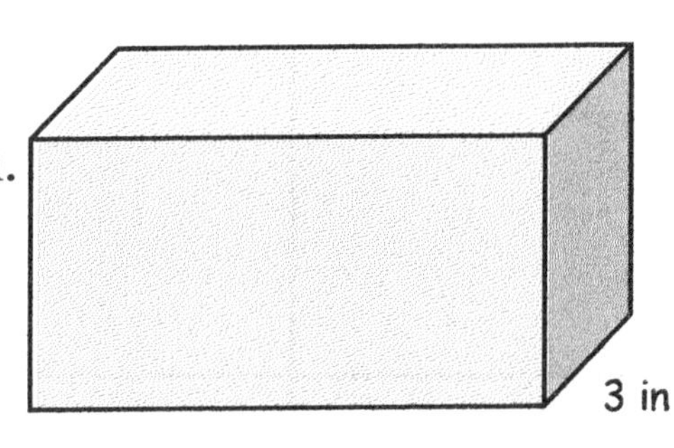

15. $8{,}050 - 4{,}361 = ?$

16. $5{,}425 \div 5 = ?$

17. $34\frac{2}{5} + 19\frac{1}{3} = ?$

18. If the radius of a circle is 45 mm, what is the diameter?

19. What do you call the middle number in an ordered set of numbers?

20. Write $\frac{57}{8}$ as a mixed number.

1.	2.	3.	4.
5.	6.	7.	8.
9.	10.	11.	12.
13.	14.	15.	16.
17.	18.	19.	20.

Lesson #91

1. $40{,}000 - 22{,}843 = ?$
2. Round \$65.41 to the nearest dollar.
3. Give the name for this type of shape.
4. $3 \times 5 \times 6 \times 2 = ?$
5. Find the area of a rectangle that is 18 m long and 10 m wide.
6. Round 53,092,906 to the nearest ten million.
7. $85 + 83 + 114 = ?$
8. $8.52 - 6.3 = ?$
9. $\frac{10}{18} \times \frac{9}{10} = ?$
10. Find the LCM of 15 and 20.
11. $12\frac{1}{7} + 7\frac{2}{3} = ?$

12. How many degrees are in a straight angle?
13. What is the length of the base of the triangle?
14. $80 \times 55 = ?$

15. Write $\frac{17}{3}$ as a mixed number.
16. $652 \div 22 = ?$
17. $3\frac{1}{5} - 1\frac{4}{5} = ?$
18. What time will it be in 8 hours and 15 minutes if it is 10:30 now?
19. Write the odd numbers between 134 and 150.
20. Megan had 30 rings. She gave $\frac{1}{5}$ of them to her best friend. How many rings does Megan have left?

1.	2.	3.	4.
5.	6.	7.	8.
9.	10.	11.	12.
13.	14.	15.	16.
17.	18.	19.	20.

Lesson #92

1. $\$100 - \$56.75 = ?$

2. How many ounces are in 4 pounds?

3. $4{,}000 \div 16 = ?$

4. Find the GCF of 12 and 21.

5. $553 + 887 = ?$

6. Which digit is in the millions place in the number 39,624,798?

7. $7\frac{1}{6} - 2\frac{2}{3} = ?$

8. List the factors of 24.

9. $4.3 - 1.21 = ?$

10. Find the average of 78, 84 and 87.

11. $5\frac{1}{2} + 2\frac{4}{5} = ?$

12. Put $\frac{8}{12}$ in simplest form.

13. How many teaspoons are in 15 tablespoons?

14. Find the perimeter of a square whose sides measure 19 yards each.

15. $900 \times 12 = ?$

16. How many centimeters are in 6 meters?

17. Jennifer used $4\frac{1}{2}$ gallons of water on her garden on Sunday and $2\frac{1}{3}$ gallons on Friday. How many total gallons did Jennifer use?

18. Explain how to find the perimeter of a regular polygon.

19. $\frac{4}{7} \times \frac{14}{20} = ?$

20. Round 321,687,904 to the nearest hundred million.

1.	2.	3.	4.
5.	6.	7.	8.
9.	10.	11.	12.
13.	14.	15.	16.
17.	18.	19.	20.

Lesson #93

1. $50{,}000 - 26{,}736 = ?$
2. Draw a pentagon. Show a line of symmetry.
3. $6 \times \frac{2}{3} = ?$
4. Which factors of 24 are also factors of 36?
5. $894 + 457 = ?$
6. It is 8:10. What time will it be in 6 hours and 5 minutes?
7. Numbers with only 2 factors are __________ numbers.
8. $16\frac{1}{4} - 12\frac{3}{4} = ?$
9. Draw perpendicular lines.
10. Write $\frac{27}{4}$ as a mixed number.
11. $\frac{6}{7} \times \frac{21}{24} = ?$
12. $92.53 - 77.8 = ?$

13. How many quarters are in 6 dollars?
14. Eleven weeks are how many days?
15. Find the mode of these numbers: 75, 121, 66, 89, 121 and 57.
16. $11\frac{4}{9} + 9\frac{2}{3} = ?$
17. $562 \div 22 = ?$
18. How many students prefer Jaguars over BMW's?
19. Mini Cooper is the favorite of how many?
20. How many students prefer Porsches or Jaguars?

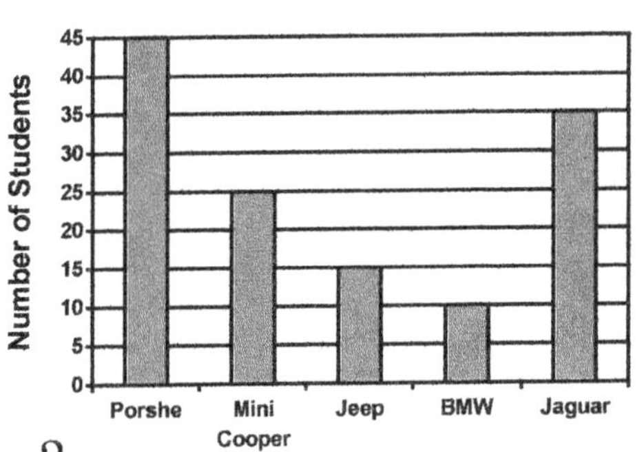

1.	2.	3.	4.
5.	6.	7.	8.
9.	10.	11.	12.
13.	14.	15.	16.
17.	18.	19.	20.

Lesson #94

1. Make a factor tree for 64.

2. How many minutes are in 6 hours?

3. $16 - 8\frac{7}{8} = ?$

4. Draw a right angle. How many degrees are in a right angle?

5. $23{,}576 + 76{,}981 = ?$

6. Round 64,875,908 to the nearest million.

7. On the Celsius temperature scale, water freezes at ______________.

8. $\frac{6}{7} \times 7 = ?$

9. How many pounds are 80 ounces?

10. $6\frac{2}{5} + 4\frac{5}{8} = ?$

11. How many centimeters are in 5 meters?

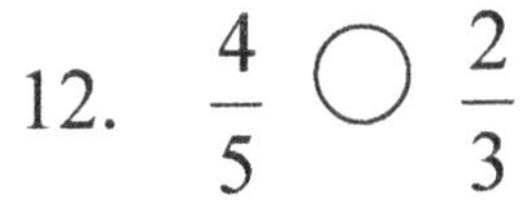

12. $\frac{4}{5} \bigcirc \frac{2}{3}$

13. Michael worked 6.5 hours on Thursday, 4.25 hours on Friday, and 5.5 hours on Saturday. How many hours did Michael work?

14. What is the average of 84, 86, 92, 95 and 98?

15. Find the perimeter and the area of a rectangle whose length is 12 ft. and whose width is 5 ft.

16. $27 \times 61 = ?$

17. Find the perimeter of this shape.

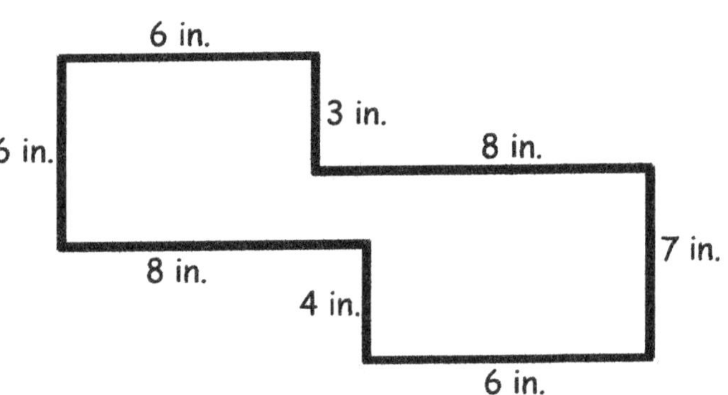

18. How many years are 4 decades?

19. $36.75 + 29.3 = ?$

20. Find the LCM of 15 and 40.

1.	2.	3.	4.
5.	6.	7.	8.
9.	10.	11.	12.
13.	14.	15.	16.
17.	18.	19.	20.

Lesson #95

1. $4,945,462 + 3,794,583 = ?$

2. What is the seventh prime number?

3. Find $\frac{3}{5}$ of 45.

4. $15,000 - 5,972 = ?$

5. Figures that have the same shape and the same size are __________.

6. Rick is 3 years older than George. George is 4 years younger than Matt. If Matt is 13, how old is Rick?

7. How many pounds are $6\frac{1}{2}$ tons?

8. $\frac{5}{6} \times \frac{12}{15} = ?$

9. Draw a ray.

10. Find the GCF and LCM of 16 and 20.

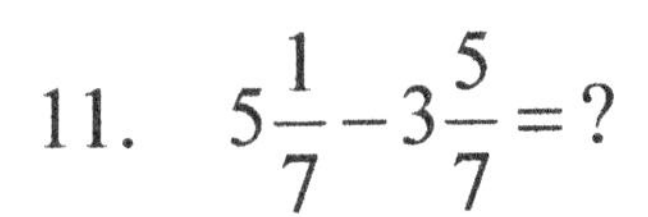

11. $5\frac{1}{7} - 3\frac{5}{7} = ?$

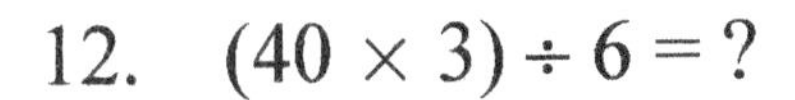

12. $(40 \times 3) \div 6 = ?$

13. Find the mode of the numbers 50, 37, 88, 50 and 67.

14. $65.6 + 44.61 = ?$

15. $\frac{4}{5} \div \frac{1}{10} = ?$

16. The top number in a fraction is called the ____________.

17. How many months are between April 10th and January 10th ?

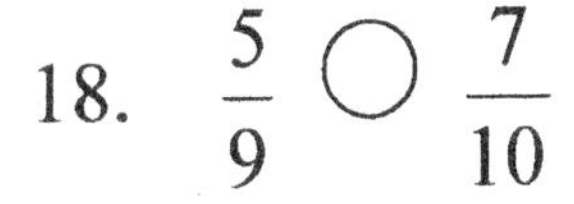

18. $\frac{5}{9} \bigcirc \frac{7}{10}$

60°F
50°F
40°F
30°F
20°F
10°F
0°F

19. Estimate the temperature shown on the thermometer.

20. This temperature (#19) is about how many degrees above freezing?

1.	2.	3.	4.
5.	6.	7.	8.
9.	10.	11.	12.
13.	14.	15.	16.
17.	18.	19.	20.

Lesson #96

1. How many pounds are 400 ounces?
2. $\frac{5}{11} \div \frac{15}{22} = ?$
3. $15 - 8\frac{1}{4} = ?$
4. How many seconds are in 3 hours?
5. Make a factor tree for 45.
6. $14\frac{2}{5} + 12\frac{1}{8} = ?$
7. My family's yard is 22 feet long and 15 feet wide. If we want to fence in our yard, how much fencing will we need?
8. $\frac{8}{9} \times \frac{12}{16} = ?$
9. What is the fifth number in the sequence? 135, 150, 165, ...
10. Write $\frac{14}{28}$ in simplest form.
11. What time was it 4 hours and 11 minutes ago, if it is 4:20 now?
12. How many milliliters are in 6 liters?
13. Find the area of a square if a side measures 15 millimeters.
14. What is the answer to a multiplication problem called?
15. 3,569 + 9,344 = ?
16. How long, in inches, is the base of the pentagon?

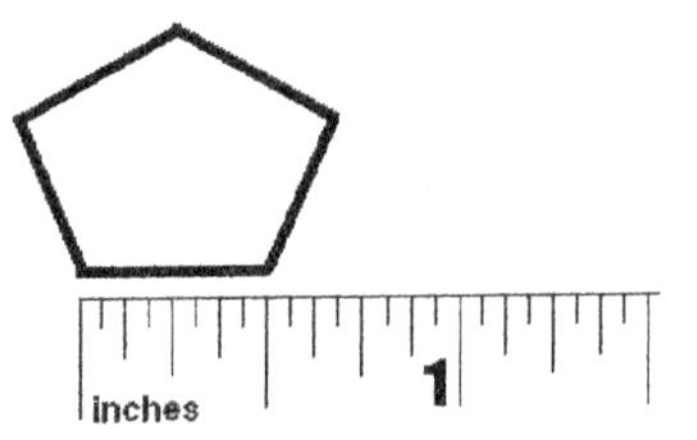

17. $60 \times 50 = ?$
18. Find the median of 24, 77, 50, 41 and 38.
19. 452 – 189 = ?
20. Five of twenty students received an A on the English test. What fraction of the students received an A on the test?

1.	2.	3.	4.
5.	6.	7.	8.
9.	10.	11.	12.
13.	14.	15.	16.
17.	18.	19.	20.

Lesson #97

1. How many feet are in 3 miles?

2. $65.71 - 24.6 = ?$

3. On the Celsius scale, water freezes at what temperature?

4. Write the name of this shape.

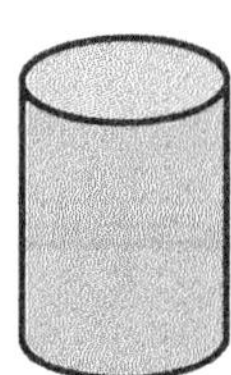

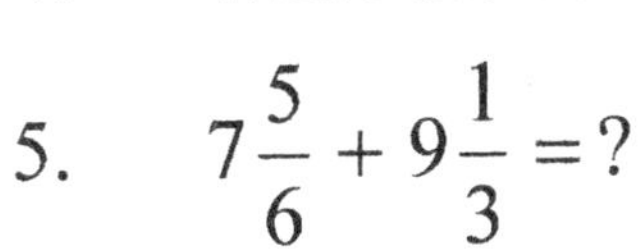

5. $7\frac{5}{6} + 9\frac{1}{3} = ?$

6. One hour and twenty minutes is how many seconds?

7. How many inches are in 4 yards?

8. Find $\frac{3}{7}$ of 21.

9. $5{,}040 - 2{,}228 = ?$

10. $\frac{5}{6} \times \frac{8}{10} = ?$

11. Draw two similar triangles.

12. List the factors of 20.

13. $25 \times 25 = ?$

14. What do we call the distance across a circle?

15. Rename $\frac{17}{6}$ as a mixed number.

16. The radius of a circle is 44 mm. What is the diameter?

17. $775 \div 50 = ?$

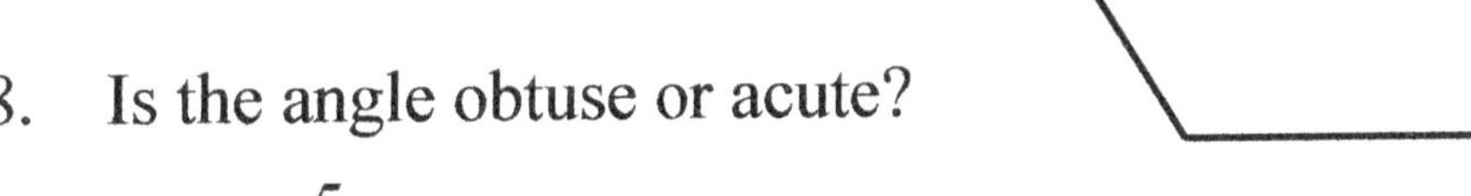

18. Is the angle obtuse or acute?

19. $17 - 9\frac{5}{6} = ?$

20. In one fifth grade class $\frac{1}{5}$ of the students wear glasses, and $\frac{1}{4}$ wear contact lenses. What fraction of the class has corrected vision?

1.	2.	3.	4.
5.	6.	7.	8.
9.	10.	11.	12.
13.	14.	15.	16.
17.	18.	19.	20.

Lesson #98

1. Round 654,796,228 to the nearest hundred million.

2. $42 \times 21 = ?$

3. How many inches are in 5 yards?

4. Explain how to find the mean (average) of a set of numbers.

5. $32{,}891 \div 6 = ?$

6. Name each polygon. A) B) C)

7. $10 - 3\frac{1}{8} = ?$

8. Draw a straight angle. How many degrees does it have?

9. $\frac{7}{8} \bigcirc \frac{5}{6}$

10. Give the estimated difference of 783 and 346.

11. $456 + 26 + 998 = ?$

12. Find the volume of the rectangular prism to the right.

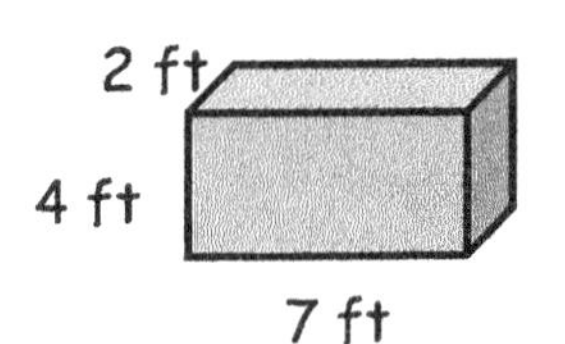

13. Find the GCF of 14 and 21.

14. Jessie needs $225 to buy a watch. She has $95. If she saves $10 each week, in how many weeks will she be able to buy the watch?

15. $\frac{5}{6} \times \frac{12}{15} = ?$

16. $13\frac{2}{3} + 24\frac{1}{5} = ?$

17. How many nickels are in $8?

18. $\frac{5}{8} \div \frac{5}{6} = ?$

19. Write $\frac{12}{20}$ in simplest terms.

20. A polygon with four sides is called a(n) ________________.

1.	2.	3.	4.
5.	6.	7.	8.
9.	10.	11.	12.
13.	14.	15.	16.
17.	18.	19.	20.

Lesson #99

1. $7\frac{1}{6} - 5\frac{5}{6} = ?$
2. Juan's height is 5 feet 4 inches. How many inches tall is Juan?
3. $44.6 + 10.8 + 21.32 = ?$
4. What fraction is shaded?

5. What is $\frac{1}{4}$ of 20?
6. How many yards are in one half of a mile?
7. The perimeter of a square is 36 inches. How long is each side?
8. $\frac{3}{5} \times \frac{10}{12} = ?$

9. How many faces does a cube have?
10. Put $\frac{8}{10}$ in simplest form.

11. Write 2.35 using words.

12. Write *five and six tenths* in standard form.
13. Kelly can buy 6 lbs of grapes for \$3.90. What is the price per pound?
14. Estimate the product of 552 and 283 by rounding to the nearest hundred.
15. $9\frac{1}{4} + 6\frac{2}{5} = ?$
16. Which digit is in the hundred thousands place in 45,607,829?
17. The radius of a circle is 8 inches. What is the diameter?
18. What is the shape of a can of beans?
19. $\frac{15}{6} \div \frac{5}{6} = ?$
20. Find the volume of this rectangular prism.

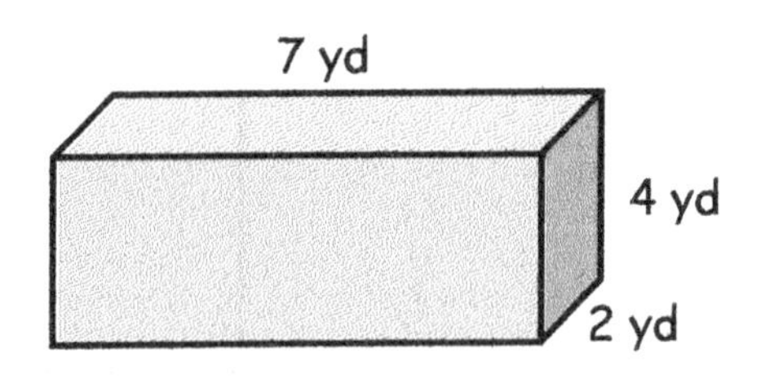

1.	2.	3.	4.
5.	6.	7.	8.
9.	10.	11.	12.
13.	14.	15.	16.
17.	18.	19.	20.

Lesson #100

1. 7,451 – 2,825 = ?

2. Find the GCF and LCM of 10 and 30.

3. The answer to a subtraction problem is the ________________.

4. (500 + 400) ÷ 30 = ?

5. Bethany went to play practice from 4:30 p.m. to 7:00 p.m. For how many minutes did she practice for the play?

6. Make a factor tree for 81.

7. $\frac{4}{5} \times \frac{5}{8} = ?$

8. Round $5.98 to the nearest dollar.

9. How many cups are in 7 pints?

10. $8\frac{4}{7} + 2\frac{1}{14} = ?$

11. Write 0.9 using words.

12. 5.6 + 7.43 + 5.8 = ?

13. A six-sided shape is a(n) ____________.

14. 92 × 33 = ?

15. $16\frac{5}{8} + 11\frac{7}{8} = ?$

16. Find the area of the rectangle.

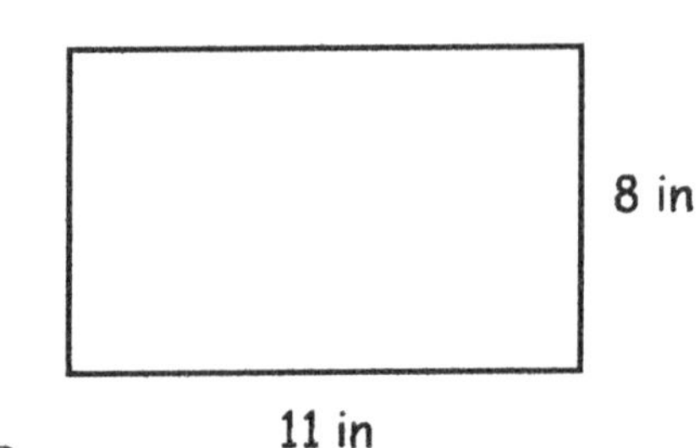

17. How many teaspoons are in 8 tablespoons?

18. A roller coaster requires riders to be at least 48 inches tall. Ted is 3 feet 5 inches tall. Can Ted ride the roller coaster? If not, how much does he have to grow before he can ride the roller coaster?

19. Change $\frac{75}{8}$ to a mixed number.

20. Write *eight and seven tenths* as a decimal.

1.	2.	3.	4.
5.	6.	7.	8.
9.	10.	11.	12.
13.	14.	15.	16.
17.	18.	19.	20.

Lesson #101

1. $881 + 395 = ?$

2. Find $\frac{5}{6}$ of 42.

3. How many days are in 2 years?

4. Round 823,798,261 to the nearest million.

5. Write the formula for finding the area of a square.

6. $17\frac{3}{5} + 12\frac{1}{4} = ?$

7. Draw a rectangle. Then show two lines of symmetry on it.

8. $\frac{5}{7} \times \frac{14}{15} = ?$

9. Which factors of 16 are also factors of 24?

10. Is 29 a prime or a composite number?

11. Write 25.81 using words.

12. $65.6 - 39.84 = ?$

13. $\frac{5}{6} \div \frac{5}{2} = ?$

14. $\frac{9}{10} \bigcirc \frac{8}{9}$

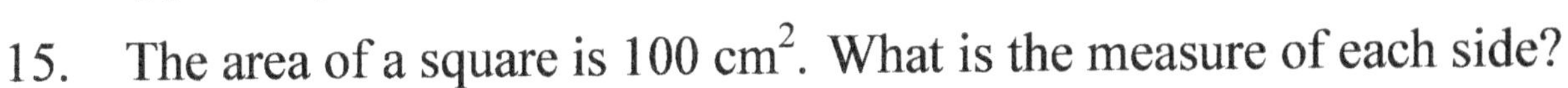

15. The area of a square is 100 cm^2. What is the measure of each side?

16. How many feet are in 4 miles?

17. Write *twelve and twenty eight hundredths* as a decimal.

18. Estimate the product of 93 and 45.

19. Round 34.65 to the nearest tenth.

20. At 8:00 a.m. the temperature was 38°F. At noon, it was 61°F. By 5:00 p.m. the thermometer read 72°F. What was the change in temperature from morning to 5:00? From morning to noon?

1.	2.	3.	4.
5.	6.	7.	8.
9.	10.	11.	12.
13.	14.	15.	16.
17.	18.	19.	20.

Lesson #102

1. Round 56.783 to the nearest hundredth.
2. How many yards are in a mile?
3. Round 43,796,091 to the nearest ten million.
4. Find the average of 68, 72, 68, 76 and 76.
5. $86.7 - 55.39 = ?$
6. Find $\frac{2}{3}$ of 27.
7. $\frac{4}{5} \times \frac{15}{16} = ?$
8. $35\frac{5}{9} + 24\frac{4}{9} = ?$
9. Write 67.09 using words.
10. Find the LCM of 12 and 18.
11. $2\frac{1}{4} \div 4\frac{1}{2} = ?$
12. Which is greater, 104 weeks or 3 years?
13. Ian is 5 feet 7 inches tall. What is Ian's height in inches?
14. Write *thirty and seven thousandths* as a decimal.
15. $\frac{5}{6} \bigcirc \frac{9}{11}$
16. Mrs. Fedor owed the plumber \$180. If she has already paid $\frac{1}{3}$ of the amount owed, how much does Mrs. Fedor still owe the plumber?
17. **A triangle with all 3 sides having the same length is called an equilateral triangle.** Draw an equilateral triangle and label each side 5 inches.

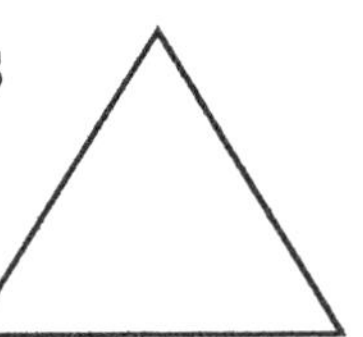

18. $743 + 896 = ?$
19. On a Fahrenheit thermometer, water boils at __________.
20. How many inches are in 2 yards?

1.	2.	3.	4.
5.	6.	7.	8.
9.	10.	11.	12.
13.	14.	15.	16.
17.	18.	19.	20.

Lesson #103

1. A triangle with all sides congruent is a(n) ___________ triangle.
2. Which digit is in the hundredths place in 12.49?
3. The area of a square is $81cm^2$. What is the length of each side?
4. A straight angle has how many degrees?
5. Estimate the product of 389 and 621.
6. $652 \div 30 = ?$
7. $5{,}000 - 2{,}569 = ?$
8. List the factors of 18.
9. $\frac{5}{7} \times \frac{14}{20} = ?$
10. Write 16.78 using words.
11. 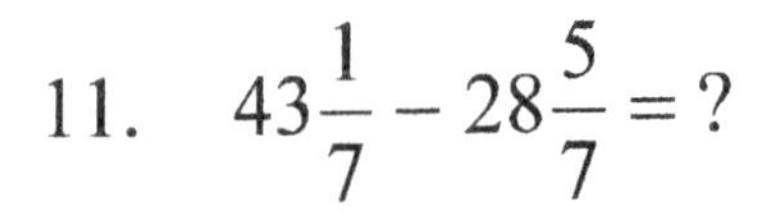
$43\frac{1}{7} - 28\frac{5}{7} = ?$
12. $25{,}679 + 88{,}562 = ?$
13. 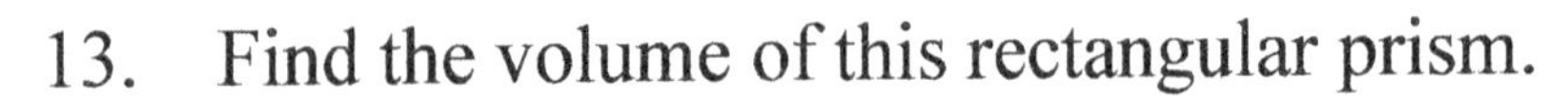
Find the volume of this rectangular prism.

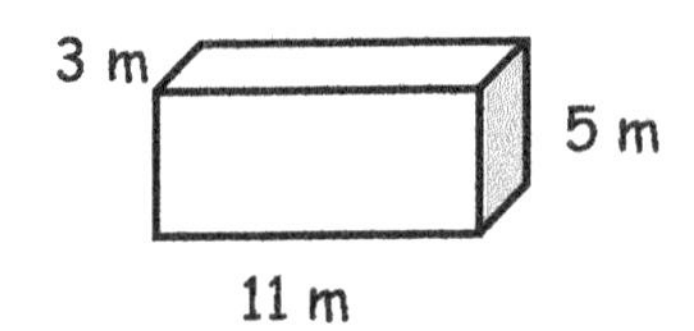

14. 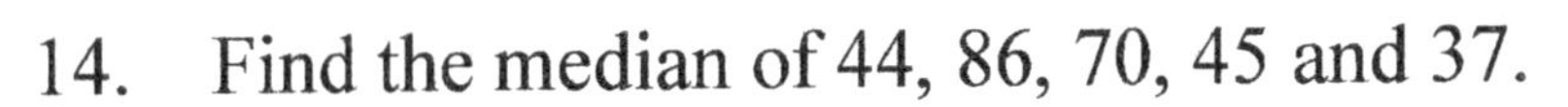
Find the median of 44, 86, 70, 45 and 37.
15. In a class of 25 students $\frac{3}{5}$ are boys. How many students are boys? How many girls are in the class?
16. If it is 2:30 now, what time will it be in 6 hours and 15 minutes?
17. How many years are in 9 centuries?
18. How many centimeters are in 5 meters?
19. Round 35.68 to the nearest tenth.
20. Use the graph to answer the questions.
    a. Name the shape located at (3, 2).
    b. Name the shape located at (1, 4).
    c. Give the pair of numbers that locates the triangle.

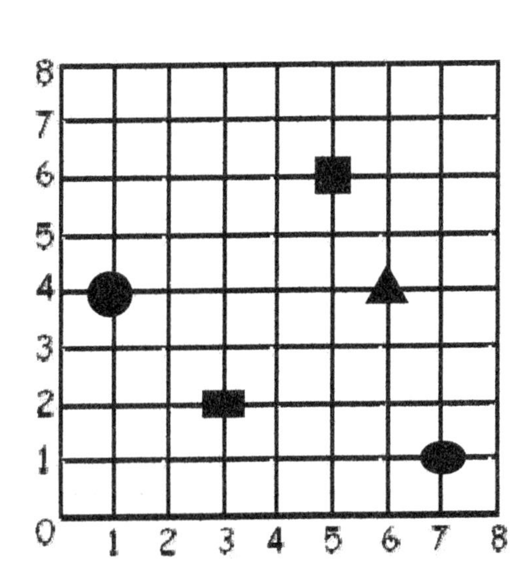

1.	2.	3.	4.
5.	6.	7.	8.
9.	10.	11.	12.
13.	14.	15.	16.
17.	18.	19.	20.

Lesson #104

1. Make a factor tree for 81.
2. Round 321.56 to the nearest tenth.
3. The answer to a multiplication problem is the ____________.
4. $965 + 873 + 122 = ?$
5. Find $\frac{3}{4}$ of 24.
6. $11\frac{1}{4} - 7\frac{5}{8} = ?$
7. How many ounces are in 5 pounds?
8. Write $\frac{39}{5}$ as a mixed number.
9. Draw a ray.
10. $133 \times 24 = ?$

11. Write *sixteen and forty-three hundredths* in decimal form.
12. Find the perimeter of the rectangle on the right.

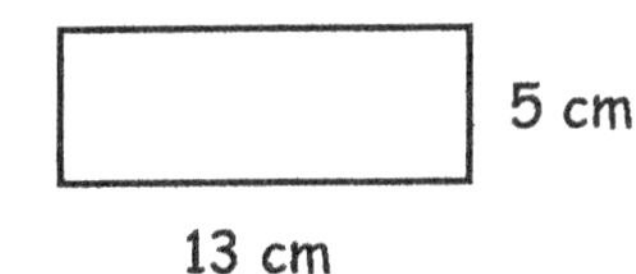

13. $\frac{2}{3} \div 1\frac{1}{3} = ?$
14. On the Celsius temperature scale, water boils at ___________.
15. A five-sided shape is called a(n) _______________.
16. Which digit is in the thousandths place in 5.098?
17. Which factors of 12 are also factors of 16?
18. $9{,}563 \div 6 = ?$
19. $654 - 288 = ?$
20. Which letter names the point (2, 4)?
    Which letter names the point (4, 1)?
    Which pair of numbers locates point A?

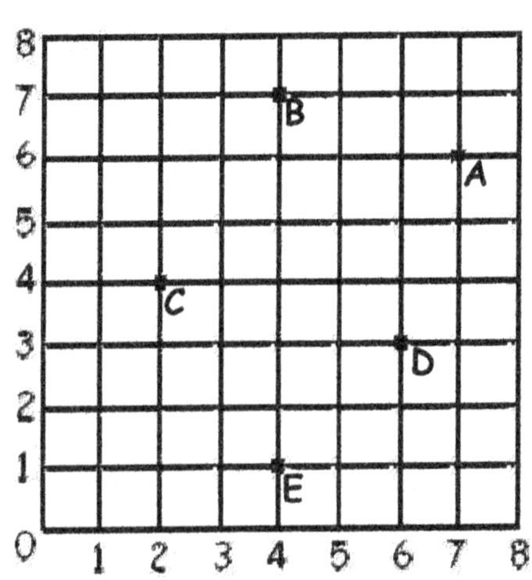

1.	2.	3.	4.
5.	6.	7.	8.
9.	10.	11.	12.
13.	14.	15.	16.
17.	18.	19.	20.

Lesson #105

1. **Triangles with no congruent sides are called scalene triangles.** Write *scalene* in the box.
2. $64.53 + 51.9 = ?$
3. Write *seven and three hundred nine thousandths* in standard form.
4. Draw perpendicular lines.

5. Find $\frac{4}{5}$ of 30.
6. $12 - 9\frac{3}{4} = ?$
7. $6{,}000 - 2{,}333 = ?$
8. $\frac{8}{9} \times \frac{9}{16} = ?$
9. Which digit is in the tenths place in 6.08?
10. How many years are in 4 decades?
11. The area of a square is 49 ft^2. What is the length of each side?
12. Round 22.458 to the nearest hundredth.
13. How many teaspoons are in 7 tablespoons?
14. Find the LCM of 12 and 15.
15. It is 5:00 now. What time was it 8 hours ago?
16. Write 32.16 using words.
17. Write the formula for finding the volume of a prism.
18. $56\frac{1}{8} + 41\frac{2}{5} = ?$
19. Draw a line segment.
20. Henry earns \$350 per week. If he saves $\frac{1}{5}$ of his weekly earnings, how much will he save each week? How much can he spend?

1.	2.	3.	4.
5.	6.	7.	8.
9.	10.	11.	12.
13.	14.	15.	16.
17.	18.	19.	20.

Lesson #106

1. Round 635,548,920 to the nearest million.

2. A triangle with no congruent sides is a(n) _______ triangle.

3. $50 \times 85 = ?$

4. Which digit is in the tenths place in 8.24?

5. Sixteen liters is how many milliliters?

6. On a Fahrenheit thermometer, water freezes at ____________.

7. Find $\frac{2}{3}$ of 18.

8. $18\frac{1}{9} - 12\frac{2}{3} = ?$

9. $351{,}886 + 465{,}725 = ?$

10. Round 56.86 to the nearest tenth.

11. $\frac{5}{7} \times \frac{21}{25} = ?$

12. List the first four prime numbers.

13. $\frac{3}{10} \div \frac{4}{5} = ?$

14. Betsy has a rope that is 6 feet in length. If she divides the rope into $1\frac{1}{2}$ foot sections, how many sections of rope will Betsy have?

Find the ordered pair for each building.

15. School ➡ _______________

16. Grocery ➡ _______________

17. Library ➡ _______________

18. Bank ➡ _______________

19. Mall ➡ _______________

20. Stadium ➡ _______________

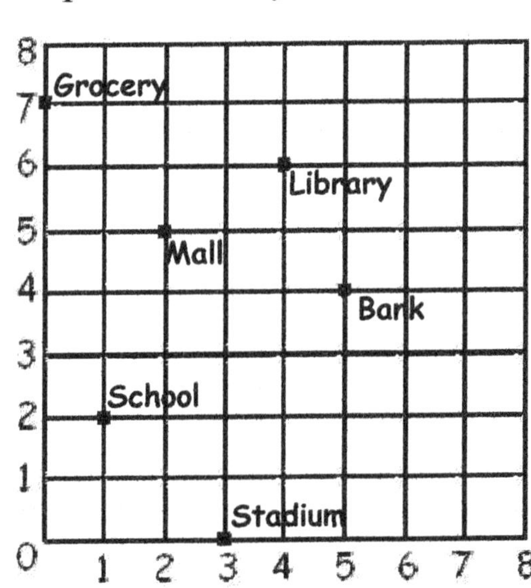

1.	2.	3.	4.
5.	6.	7.	8.
9.	10.	11.	12.
13.	14.	15.	16.
17.	18.	19.	20.

Lesson #107

1. $8\frac{1}{6} + 7\frac{2}{3} = ?$

2. How many yards are in a mile?

3. $17\frac{1}{7} - 6\frac{4}{7} = ?$

4. Write 84.51 using words.

5. $128.9 - 75.76 = ?$

6. List the factors of 24.

7. $500 - 198 = ?$

8. $\frac{4}{9} \times \frac{18}{20} = ?$

9. Write *sixteen and thirty-seven hundredths* as a decimal.

10. Which is greater, 0.56 or 0.641?

11. A triangle with no congruent sides is ________________.

12. $\frac{3}{5} \bigcirc \frac{7}{10}$

13. What do we call a four-sided polygon?

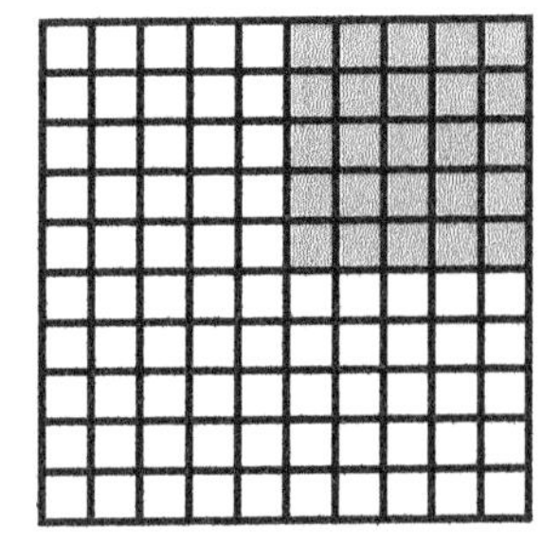

14. Look at the figure to the right. Write a decimal for the part that is shaded.

15. How many days are in 7 weeks?

16. Is the number 71 a prime or a composite number?

17. Reduce $\frac{5}{10}$ to simplest form.

18. Find the volume of the rectangular prism.

15 cm
5 cm
3 cm

19. The Boy Scouts took orders for 480 key chains. If they make 24 key chains per day, how long will it take them to fill their orders?

20. Which digit is in the hundred thousands place in 12,386,957?

1.	2.	3.	4.
5.	6.	7.	8.
9.	10.	11.	12.
13.	14.	15.	16.
17.	18.	19.	20.

Lesson #108

1. Write 67.804 using words.

2. How many ounces are in 5 pounds?

3. $40{,}000 - 26{,}988 = ?$

4. $18\frac{5}{6} + 23\frac{1}{3} = ?$

5. These are David's social studies test scores for the first quarter: 92, 88, 85, 84, 91 and 70. What was David's average for social studies?

6. $54.63 + 49.6 = ?$

7. **An isosceles triangle has 2 congruent sides.** Write *isosceles.*

8. Any number multiplied by zero has an answer of ______________.

9. Find the area of a square if a side measures 18 meters.

10. Find the GCF of 10 and 25.

11. $15\frac{7}{8} - 10\frac{3}{4} = ?$

12. $\frac{6}{8} \div \frac{3}{8} = ?$

13. How many feet are in 3 miles?

14. $22 \times 44 = ?$

15. Put these decimals in order from greatest to least.

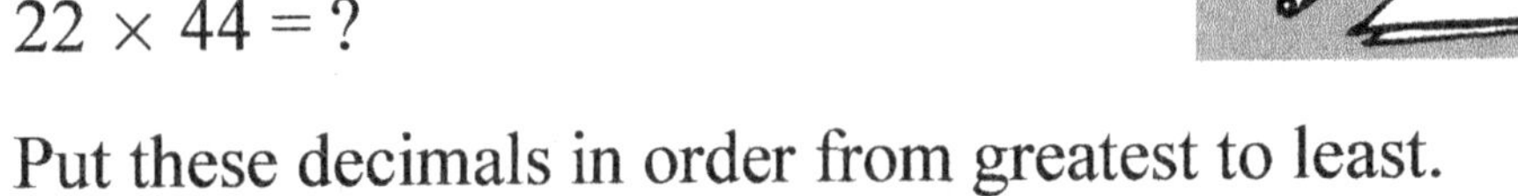

3.67 3.067 3.76 3.006

16. Estimate the difference of 985 and 344.

17. What part is shaded? Write your answer as a fraction and a decimal.

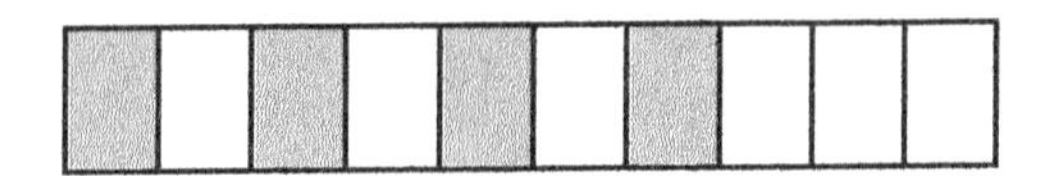

18. Make a factor tree for 56.

19. A polygon with eight sides is a(n) ______________.

20. $545 \div 21 = ?$

1.	2.	3.	4.
5.	6.	7.	8.
9.	10.	11.	12.
13.	14.	15.	16.
17.	18.	19.	20.

Lesson #109

1. Draw an acute angle.
2. $60,000 - 34,518 = ?$
3. How many centimeters are in 6 meters?
4. Find the area and the perimeter of the rectangle.

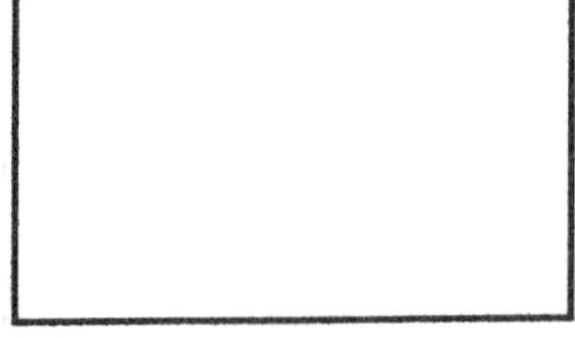

5. $5.6 \times 0.3 = ?$
6. $41\frac{5}{6} - 27\frac{2}{3} = ?$
7. Find the LCM of 15 and 25.
8. $85 + 19 + 168 = ?$
9. How many quarts are in 4 gallons?
10. Reduce $\frac{9}{12}$ to simplest terms.
11. Write 0.5421 in words.
12. $\frac{5}{7} \times \frac{1}{5} = ?$
13. Find $\frac{2}{3}$ of 24.
14. $45.35 \div 0.05 = ?$
15. $33 \times 52 = ?$

16. Write $\frac{31}{4}$ as a mixed number.
17. A triangle that has 2 congruent sides is called a(n) _______ triangle.
18. Round 6.892 to the nearest hundredth.
19. Which is greater, 60 inches or 6 feet?
20. Janice works $\frac{1}{3}$ of her day at a hospital and $\frac{1}{8}$ of her day at the mall. How many hours does she work at the hospital? At the mall?

1.	2.	3.	4.
5.	6.	7.	8.
9.	10.	11.	12.
13.	14.	15.	16.
17.	18.	19.	20.

Lesson #110

1. A five-sided shape is a(n) _______________.

2. $4{,}812 \times 4 = ?$

3. Find the mode of 89, 35, 20, 66 and 35.

4. Which digit is in the tenths place in 36.9072?

5. $775 \div 35 = ?$

6. Round 736,576,302 to the nearest hundred million.

7. How many degrees make up a straight angle?

8. $18{,}952 + 47{,}586 = ?$

9. Rewrite $\frac{15}{20}$ in simplest form.

10. $0.8 - 0.195 = ?$

11. Find $\frac{2}{5}$ of 50.

12. $6.55 \div 0.5 = ?$

13. List the factors of 24.

14. $0.008 \times 0.09 = ?$

15. Is 13 a prime or a composite number?

16. Write *ten and three thousandths* in standard decimal form.

17. $62\frac{1}{8} + 41\frac{2}{5} = ?$

18. Figures with the same size and shape are _____________.

19. Put these decimals in order from least to greatest.
    0.6   0.04   0.178   0.022

20. Jason earned \$65 at work last week. He put $\frac{1}{5}$ of his earnings in a savings account. How much did he save?

1.	2.	3.	4.
5.	6.	7.	8.
9.	10.	11.	12.
13.	14.	15.	16.
17.	18.	19.	20.

Lesson #111

1. $62 \times 23 = ?$

2. Write $8\frac{3}{7}$ as an improper fraction.

3. $4\frac{3}{4} + 2\frac{3}{8} = ?$

4. Draw 2 congruent squares.

5. Which is greater, 6 tons or 10,000 pounds?

6. Which factors of 16 are also factors of 24?

7. $2.35 \times 0.5 = ?$

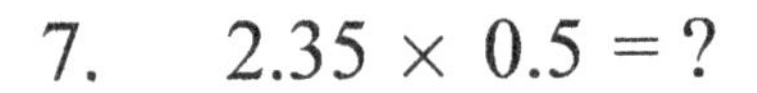

8. $9\frac{3}{5} - 5\frac{1}{4} = ?$

9. Write the formula for finding the perimeter of a regular polygon.

10. Find the average of 310, 421 and 424.

11. Which digit is in the thousandths place in 4.085?

12. If $4x = 16$, what is the value of x?

13. $\frac{5}{8} \times \frac{10}{15} = ?$

14. Closed figures made up of line segments are _______________.

15. $25\frac{1}{5} - 16\frac{3}{5} = ?$

16. The temperature at 7 a.m. was 25°F. At 3 p.m., it was 30° warmer; by 8 p.m. it had fallen by 25°. What was the temperature at 8 p.m.?

17. Is this a slide, a rotation, or a reflection?

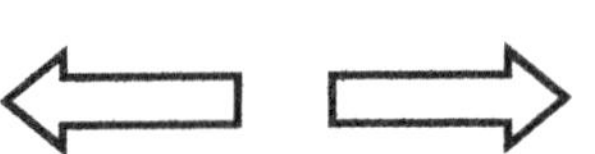

18. Round 68.931 to the nearest hundredth.

19. What do you call the distance across the middle of a circle?

20. $8.42 \div 0.02 = ?$

1.	2.	3.	4.
5.	6.	7.	8.
9.	10.	11.	12.
13.	14.	15.	16.
17.	18.	19.	20.

Lesson #112

1. Write 15.067 in words.
2. $40{,}000 - 23{,}891 = ?$
3. What time was it 7 hours and 15 minutes ago, if it is 1:15 now?
4. How many years are in 5 decades?
5. Round 526,897,560 to the nearest ten million.
6. $56.75 + 9.22 + 24.66 = ?$
7. Put these decimals in order from least to greatest.
   12.45 12.045 12.54 12.054
8. Round 84.924 to the nearest hundredth.

9. $2\frac{1}{2} \times 3\frac{1}{10} = ?$
10. Find the GCF of 14 and 21.
11. Find $\frac{3}{5}$ of 45.
12. $2.67 \times 0.04 = ?$
13. $\frac{9}{10} \div \frac{3}{10} = ?$
14. $35.65 \div 0.05 = ?$
15. Figures having the same shape, but different size are ____________.
16. $56\frac{1}{6} - 29\frac{5}{6} = ?$
17. **This shape is a parallelogram.** ▱ **It has 2 sets of parallel sides.** Draw a parallelogram in the box.
18. Which digit is in the thousandths place in 4.008?
19. $\frac{5}{9} \bigcirc \frac{4}{7}$
20. If a lion weighs 225 pounds 5 ounces, how many ounces does it weigh?

1.	2.	3.	4.
5.	6.	7.	8.
9.	10.	11.	12.
13.	14.	15.	16.
17.	18.	19.	20.

Lesson #113

1. Draw a parallelogram.
2. Make a factor tree for 48.
3. $56{,}782 + 34{,}927 = ?$
4. How many years are in 9 centuries?
5. Draw a right angle. How many degrees are in a right angle?
6. Write 7.3201 using words.
7. $\frac{8}{10} \div \frac{2}{10} = ?$
8. Round 89.573 to the nearest tenth.
9. Write $\frac{19}{2}$ as a mixed number.
10. $2\frac{1}{6} \times 3\frac{1}{3} = ?$
11. $70{,}000 - 48{,}365 = ?$

12. How many inches are in 6 yards?

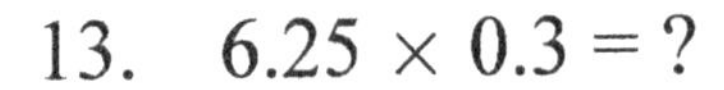

13. $6.25 \times 0.3 = ?$
14. $1.44 \div 6 = ?$

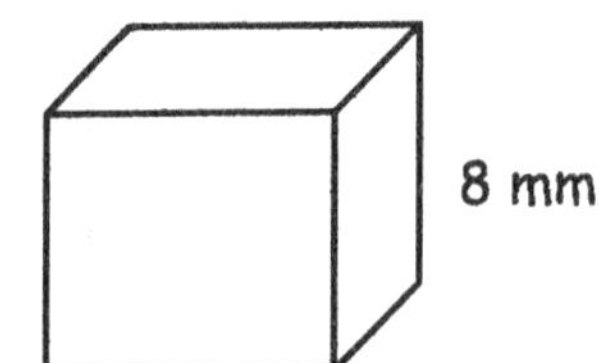

15. Find the volume of this cube.
16. Find the LCM of 12 and 20.
17. $\frac{3}{4} + \frac{5}{8} = ?$
18. Half of the diameter is called the ________.
19. 0.567 ◯ 0.6
20. Daniel bought a TV for \$595, a DVD-player for \$69, and 5 DVD's that cost \$15.95 each. What is the <u>estimated</u> total for Daniel's purchases?

1.	2.	3.	4.
5.	6.	7.	8.
9.	10.	11.	12.
13.	14.	15.	16.
17.	18.	19.	20.

Lesson #114

1. All four-sided shapes are called ______________.

2. Put these decimals in order from greatest to least.

   1.32 1.032 1.325 1.302

3. In a bag of marbles, 4 are blue, 2 are white, 3 are red, and 1 is black. Give the probability of picking a blue one? Red? Green?

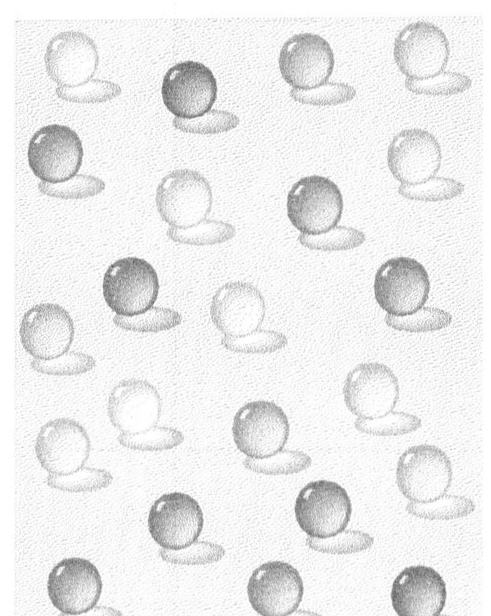

4. 45,783 – 21,566 = ?

5. $17\frac{1}{9} - 9\frac{7}{9} = ?$

6. How many quarts are in 4 gallons?

7. 2.809 ◯ 2.9

8. $\frac{5}{6} \times \frac{18}{20} = ?$

9. $3.26 \times 0.03 = ?$

10. 9 tablespoons contain how many teaspoons?

11. Round 34,568,992 to the nearest thousand.

12. Figures with the same size and the same shape are ______________.

13. Which digit is in the hundredths place in 15.723?

14. 0.8 – 0.4673 = ?

15. Find the area of this parallelogram.

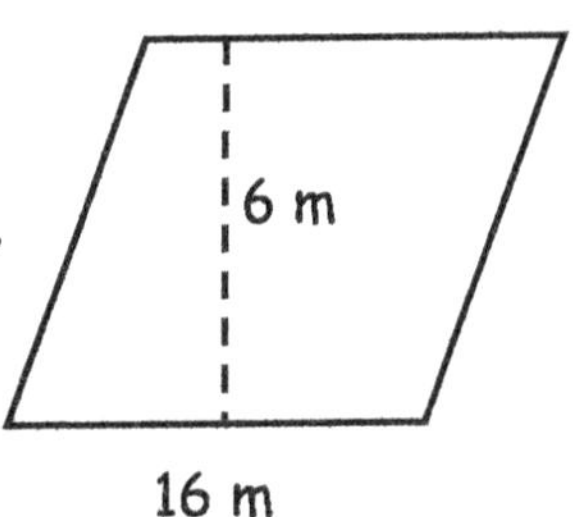

16. 26.25 ÷ 7 = ?

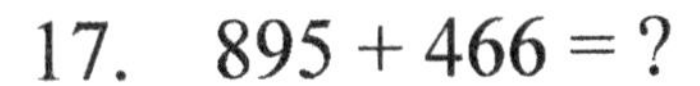

17. 895 + 466 = ?

18. Write the decimal number for *eight and five thousandths.*

19. Karen worked $6\frac{1}{2}$ hours on Monday, $4\frac{1}{2}$ hours on Tuesday, and $5\frac{1}{4}$ on Wednesday. How many total hours did Karen work?

20. $88 \times 22 = ?$

1.	2.	3.	4.
5.	6.	7.	8.
9.	10.	11.	12.
13.	14.	15.	16.
17.	18.	19.	20.

Lesson #115

40°F
30°F
20°F
10°F
0°F
-10°F
-20°F

1. How many cups are in 6 pints?
2. $1\frac{1}{3}+1\frac{1}{6}=?$
3. What temperature is shown on the thermometer?
4. $5.62 + 0.8 + 3.0 = ?$
5. $11-5\frac{2}{9}=?$
6. $3{,}888 \div 36 = ?$
7. Draw an obtuse angle. Does it measure more or less than 90°?
8. What is the probability of getting a 4 on one roll of a die?
9. $208.4 \div 0.8 = ?$
10. Find the area of the parallelogram.

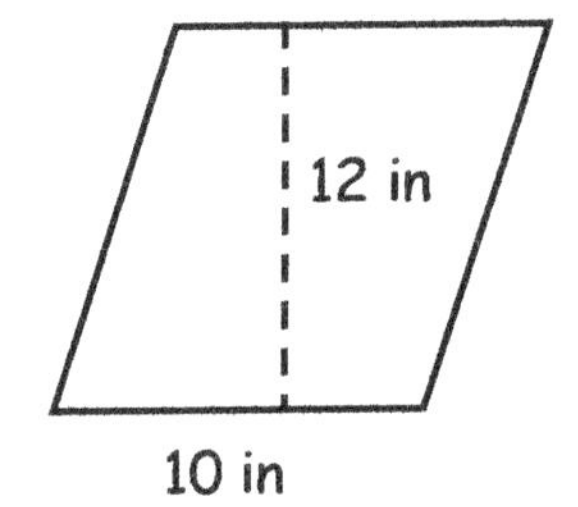

11. $0.007 \times 0.009 = ?$
12. If $7x = 49$, what is the value of x?
13. $\frac{5}{6}\times\frac{12}{25}=?$
14. Find the GCF of 15 and 25.
15. $34{,}702 \times 4 = ?$
16. Make a factor tree for 90.
17. Write $\frac{78}{9}$ as a mixed number.

18. Write the formula for finding the volume of a prism.
19. Is 71 a prime or a composite number?
20. It costs \$1.75 for the first hour to park in the city parking lot. It costs \$.75 for every half hour after that. How much did Mr. Morgan have to pay to park in the lot for $3\frac{1}{2}$ hours?

1.	2.	3.	4.
5.	6.	7.	8.
9.	10.	11.	12.
13.	14.	15.	16.
17.	18.	19.	20.

Lesson #116

1. What is the name for the number that occurs most often in a list?

2. Find the LCM of 15 and 20.

3. $\frac{4}{7} + \frac{3}{7} = ?$

4. Find $\frac{4}{5}$ of 50.

5. 0.785 ◯ 0.85

6. $\frac{4}{8} \div \frac{2}{8} = ?$

7. How many centimeters are in 15 meters?

8. Write the formula for finding the area of a parallelogram.

9. Find the perimeter and the area of this rectangle.

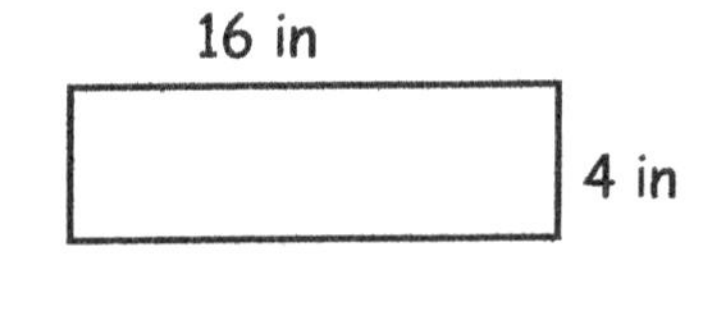

10. Write $8\frac{5}{8}$ as an improper fraction.

11. Name this shape.

12. $\frac{2}{3} \times \frac{3}{10} = ?$

13. Write *thirty and seventeen hundredths* in decimal form.

14. $22.78 \times 0.03 = ?$

15. On the Fahrenheit temperature scale, water boils at _____________.

16. On the Celsius temperature scale, water boils at _____________.

17. Which digit is in the ten thousandths place in 45.6079?

For 18 - 20, identify each as a slide, a rotation or a reflection.

18. 

19. 

20. 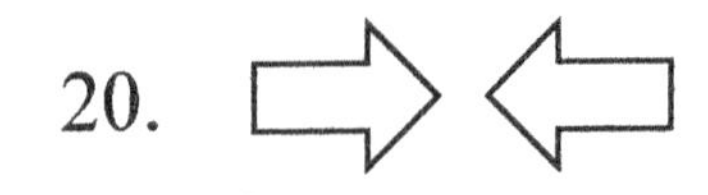

1.	2.	3.	4.
5.	6.	7.	8.
9.	10.	11.	12.
13.	14.	15.	16.
17.	18.	19.	20.

Lesson #117

1. $45.68 \div 0.02 = ?$

2. The area of a square is 81 mm^2. What is the length of each side?

3. $56.7 + 7.35 + 0.142 = ?$

4. Find the average and the mode of 52, 34, 62, 23, 71 and 52.

5. Write the formula for finding the area of a rectangle.

6. Give the estimated difference of 815 and 278.

7. Name this shape.

8. Find $\frac{4}{5}$ of 35.

9. 0.3 ◯ 0.12

10. Write the decimal number for *twenty-eight and fifty-three hundredths.*

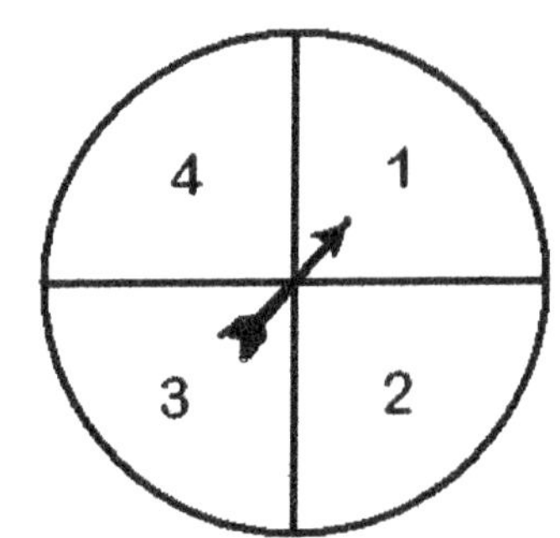

11. What is the probability of the spinner landing on a number less than 4?

12. Find the LCM of 6, 8 and 15.

13. Round 16.079 to the nearest tenth.

14. How many feet are in 5 miles?

15. $33\frac{2}{5} + 17\frac{1}{2} = ?$

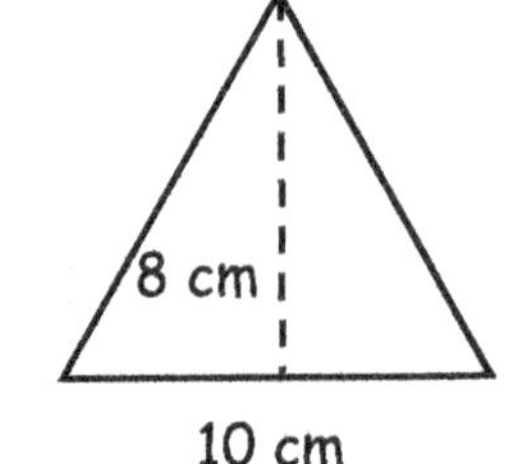

16. $0.04 \times 0.06 = ?$

17. Find the area of the triangle. *See the Help Pages for examples.*

18. Draw a parallelogram.

19. What do you call the bottom number in a fraction?

20. In November, Mr. Torrez sold 25 cars during the 1st week, 38 cars during the 2nd week, and 51 cars during the 3rd week. At this rate, how many cars will he sell during the 1st week of December?

1.	2.	3.	4.
5.	6.	7.	8.
9.	10.	11.	12.
13.	14.	15.	16.
17.	18.	19.	20.

Lesson #118

1. 14.007 ◯ 14.107
2. Find the difference of $\frac{3}{4}$ and $\frac{1}{3}$.
3. $(14 \div 2) \times 6 = ?$
4. Which digit is in the hundredths place in 6.8092?
5. Find $\frac{2}{3}$ of 18.
6. Andy is 6 feet 4 inches tall. What is Andy's height in inches?
7. $10\frac{3}{5} + 13\frac{1}{4} = ?$
8. Find the perimeter of an equilateral triangle if a side is 34 mm.
9. $2 \div 3\frac{1}{2} = ?$
10. If $6x = 48$, what is the value of x?
11. $27.9 - 13.75 = ?$
12. How many pounds are in $9\frac{1}{2}$ tons?
13. $0.23 \times 0.06 = ?$

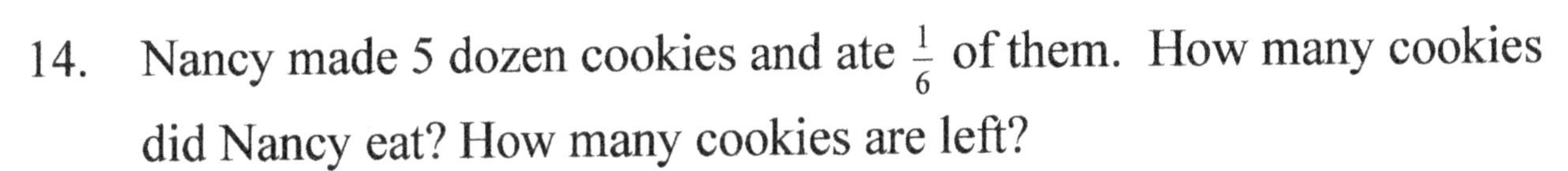

14. Nancy made 5 dozen cookies and ate $\frac{1}{6}$ of them. How many cookies did Nancy eat? How many cookies are left?
15. If it is 2:45 now, what time will it be in 5 hours and 15 minutes?
16. $4.5 \div 6 = ?$
17. Write the formula for finding the area of a triangle.
18. How many millimeters are 7 meters?
19. $88 + 19 + 67 = ?$
20. Write the reciprocal of $\frac{4}{7}$.

1.	2.	3.	4.
5.	6.	7.	8.
9.	10.	11.	12.
13.	14.	15.	16.
17.	18.	19.	20.

Lesson #119

1. Which factors of 14 are also factors of 21?
2. Write 8.704 in words.
3. Name the shape to the right.

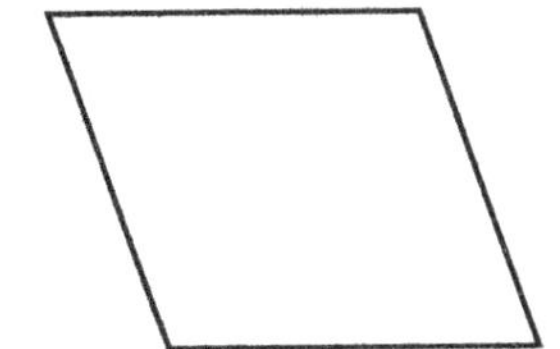

4. $(22 + 14) - (10 - 4) = ?$
5. Round 97.256 to the nearest tenth.
6. Numbers that have only two factors are ________ numbers.
7. Find the LCM of 16 and 20.
8. Find the area of the triangle.

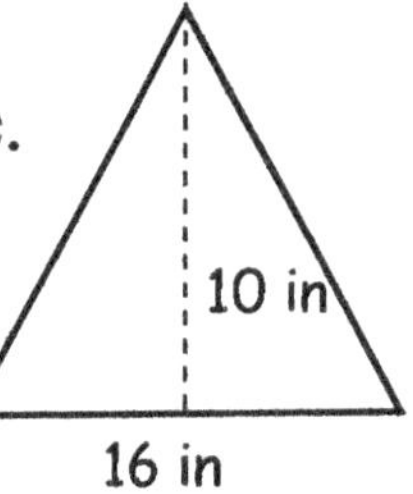

9. $14\frac{1}{6} - 10\frac{5}{6} = ?$
10. Find $\frac{5}{6}$ of 24.
11. Make a factor tree for 54.
12. $500 - 265 = ?$
13. $\frac{5}{6} \times \frac{2}{3} = ?$

14. What is the sum of the first four even numbers?
15. Explain how to find the average (mean) of a set of numbers.
16. Which digit is in the thousandths place in 3.790?
17. What is the probability of rolling a seven on one throw of a die?
18. Arrange these decimals in order from greatest to least.
    3.9 3.009 3.87 3.08
19. The sapling was 39 inches tall when it was first planted. Two years later it was 5 feet 4 inches tall. How much did the sapling grow?
20. $9,377 + 8,542 = ?$

1.	2.	3.	4.
5.	6.	7.	8.
9.	10.	11.	12.
13.	14.	15.	16.
17.	18.	19.	20.

Lesson #120

1. $5.03 \times 0.6 = ?$

2. How many minutes are in 8 hours?

3. $0.48 \div 0.08 = ?$

4. Draw a hexagon. Show a line of symmetry.

5. Write the number 3.218 using words.

6. **A triangle with no congruent sides is called a scalene triangle.** Write the word *scalene* in the box.

7. 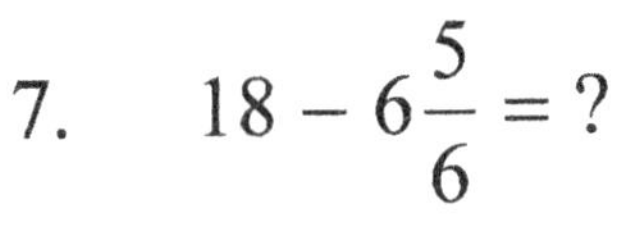 $18 - 6\frac{5}{6} = ?$

8. Find the GCF of 15 and 20.

9. 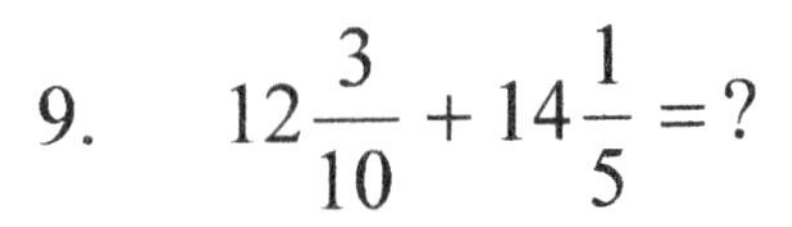 $12\frac{3}{10} + 14\frac{1}{5} = ?$

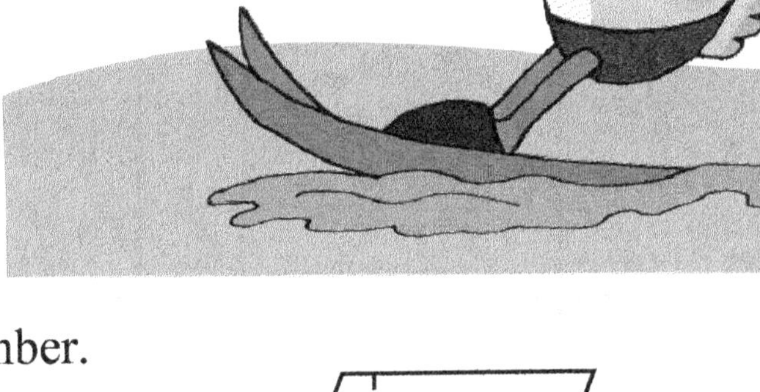

10. $67{,}899 + 32{,}476 = ?$

11. $\frac{4}{5} \times \frac{15}{16} = ?$

12. Write $\frac{23}{4}$ as a mixed number.

13. How many years are in 7 decades?

14. Find the area of the parallelogram.

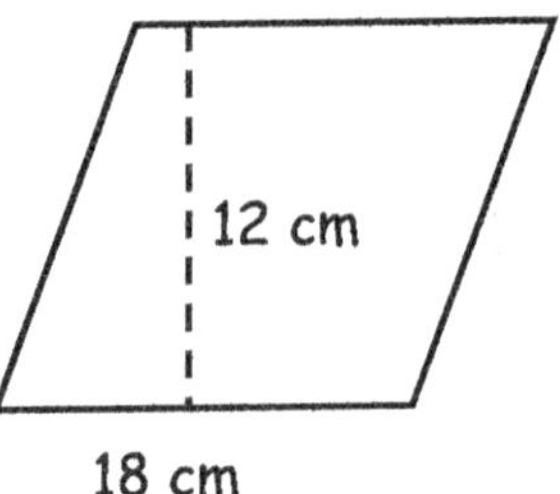

15. Round 68.082 to the nearest tenth.

16. Find the average of 16, 18, 20 and 22.

17. A triangle with two congruent sides is called ______________.

18. Willie worked 6.5 hours on Saturday and 5.5 hours on Sunday. If he earns $7.25 per hour, how much did he earn on the weekend?

19. What is the probability of an event that is certain to happen?

20. Write the formula for finding the area of a triangle.

1.	2.	3.	4.
5.	6.	7.	8.
9.	10.	11.	12.
13.	14.	15.	16.
17.	18.	19.	20.

Lesson #121

1. Draw a ray.

2. Which is greater, 2 miles or 15,840 feet?

3. How many centimeters are in 16 meters?

4. 92,786 + 557,247 = ?

5. Closed figures made up of line segments are ______________.

6. Find the median and the mode of 122, 149, 219, 184 and 219.

7. Half of the diameter of a circle is called the __________.

8. $32\frac{3}{10} + 41\frac{1}{5} = ?$

9. Find the area of the triangle.

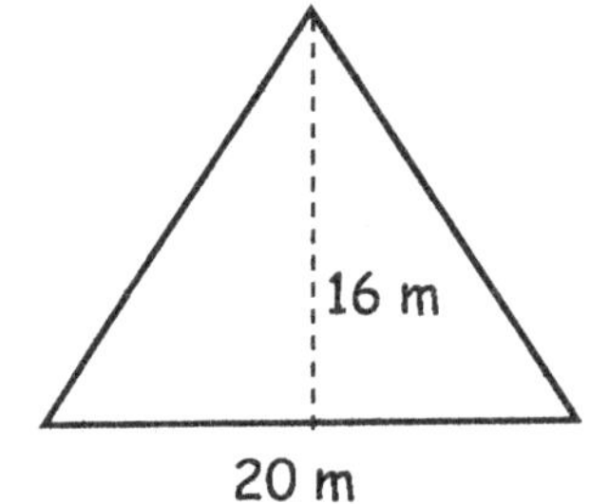

10. Find $\frac{4}{5}$ of 25.

11. **The distance around the outside of a circle is called circumference.** Write *circumference* in the box.

12. Round 57,894,216 to the nearest hundred thousand.

13. A number with only two factors is a ___________ number.

14. Round 77.849 to the nearest tenth.

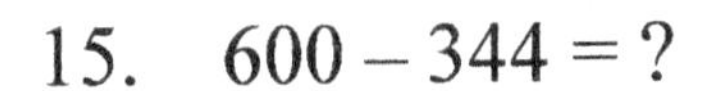

15. 600 – 344 = ?

16. $0.065 \times 0.04 = ?$

17. Write 8.312 using words.

18. $1\frac{1}{4} \div 2\frac{1}{2} = ?$

19. 9.2 – 5.783 = ?

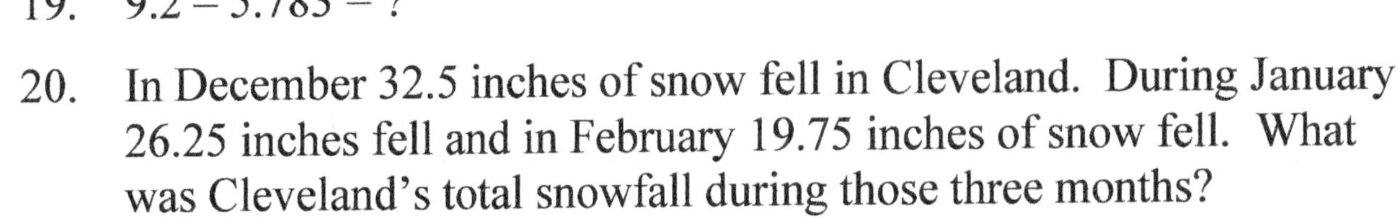

20. In December 32.5 inches of snow fell in Cleveland. During January 26.25 inches fell and in February 19.75 inches of snow fell. What was Cleveland's total snowfall during those three months?

1.	2.	3.	4.
5.	6.	7.	8.
9.	10.	11.	12.
13.	14.	15.	16.
17.	18.	19.	20.

Lesson #122

1. The answer in a subtraction problem is called the __________.

2. $\frac{6}{10} \times \frac{5}{9} = ?$

3. The distance around the outside of a circle is called ________.

4. Find the LCM of 14 and 18.

5. $(25 \times 2) + (100 - 66) = ?$

6. How many ounces are in 8 pounds?

7. A triangle with no congruent sides is called _______________.

8. $53\frac{1}{6} + 22\frac{2}{3} = ?$

9. Write the formula for finding the volume of a prism.

10. Which digit is in the thousandths place in 9.0317?

11. $\frac{9}{10} \div \frac{3}{10} = ?$

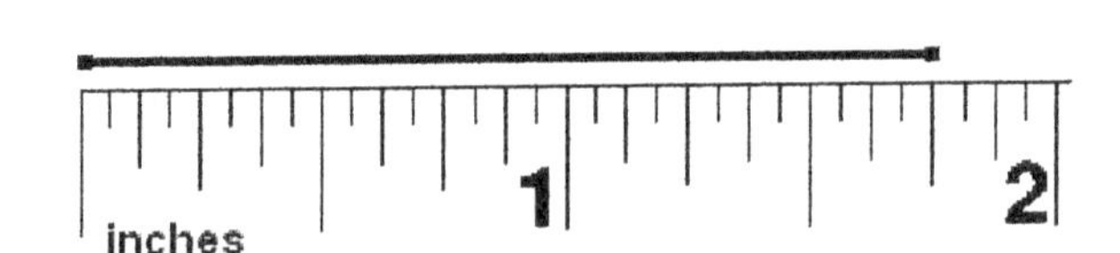

12. How long is this segment?

13. Make a factor tree for 36.

14. If Frankie earned \$8 per hour, how much will he earn if he works $2\frac{1}{2}$ hours? $3\frac{1}{4}$ hours?

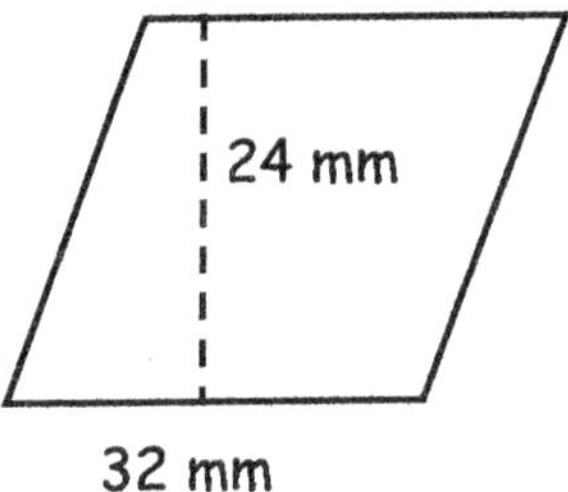

15. Find the area of the parallelogram.

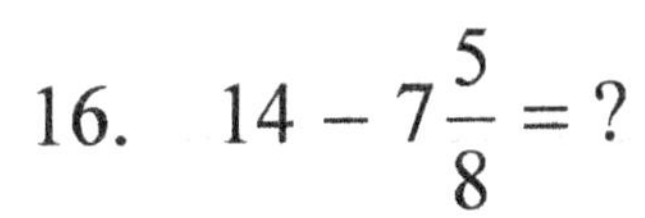

16. $14 - 7\frac{5}{8} = ?$

17. How many inches are in 5 feet?

18. $48.92 + 23.5 = ?$

19. Find the GCF of 15 and 20.

20. Figures with the same size and shape are _____________.

1.	2.	3.	4.
5.	6.	7.	8.
9.	10.	11.	12.
13.	14.	15.	16.
17.	18.	19.	20.

Lesson #123

1. What kind of angle measures less than 90°? Draw one.

2. $\frac{5}{6} \times \frac{2}{5} = ?$

3. Estimate the product of 88 and 54.

4. How many tons are 18,000 pounds?

5. Write *seven and twelve thousandths* in standard decimal form.

6. Mrs. Smith is taking herself and 15 students to a movie. The cost of each ticket was $4.25. How much did she spend on the tickets?

7. $\frac{5}{9} \bigcirc \frac{3}{10}$

8. Round 3.691 to the nearest tenth.

9. $9\frac{2}{5} + 4\frac{1}{3} = ?$

10. Put $\frac{12}{18}$ in simplest form.

11. $65 + 88 + 92 = ?$

12. How many quarts are in 6 gallons?

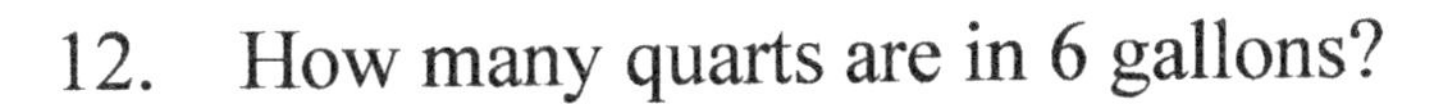

13. Find the area of Marissa's bedroom if it is 14 ft. long by 12 ft. wide.

14. $341 - 198 = ?$

15. List the factors of 20.

16. Draw intersecting lines.

17. Find the circumference of this circle.

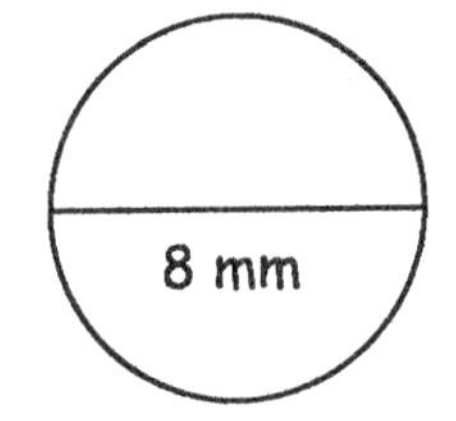

18. Is the number 23 prime or composite?

19. Order these decimals from least to greatest.
    5.23 5.3 5.02 5.323

20. What is the top number in a fraction called?

1.	2.	3.	4.
5.	6.	7.	8.
9.	10.	11.	12.
13.	14.	15.	16.
17.	18.	19.	20.

Lesson #124

1. How many minutes are in 3 hours?

2. $7 - 4\frac{5}{7} = ?$

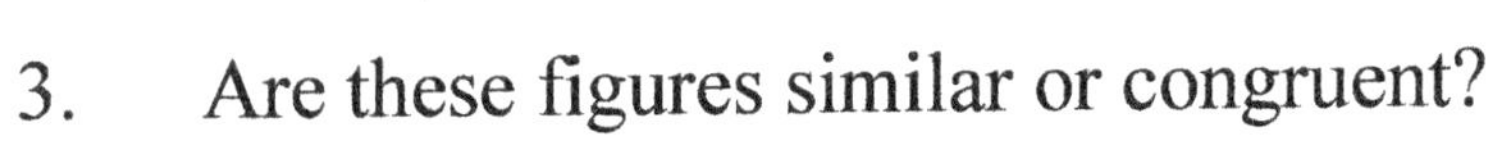

3. Are these figures similar or congruent?

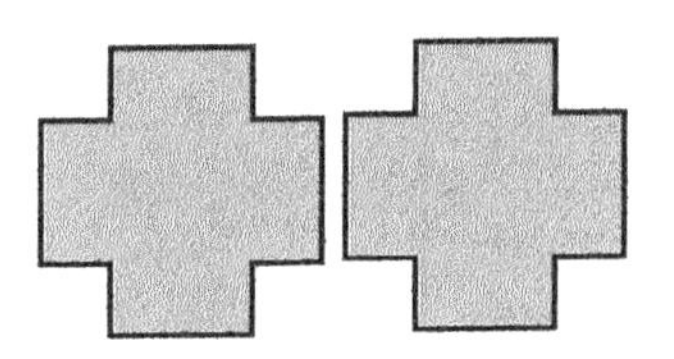

4. Find the GCF of 12 and 16.

5. A baker used 660 boxes of cake mix to make a wedding cake. If each box called for 3 eggs, how many dozen eggs were used to make the wedding cake?

6. What is the probability of rolling a five on one throw of a die?

7. $0.8 - 0.534 = ?$

8. How many yards are in a mile?

9. $0.835 \div 0.5 = ?$

10. Find $\frac{2}{9}$ of 45.

11. $41 \times 62 = ?$

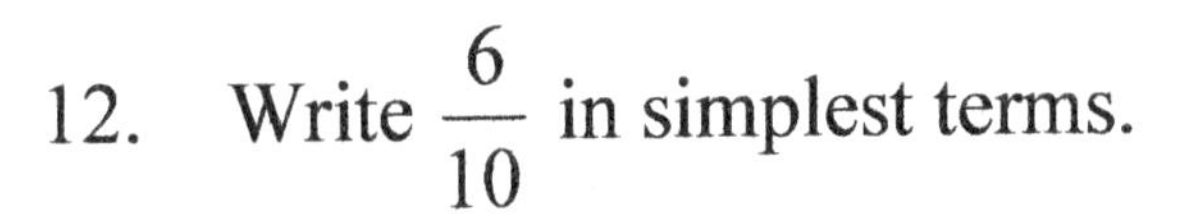

12. Write $\frac{6}{10}$ in simplest terms.

13. $5{,}679 + 3{,}662 = ?$

14. Draw perpendicular lines.

15. $(12 \times 7) \div 4 = ?$

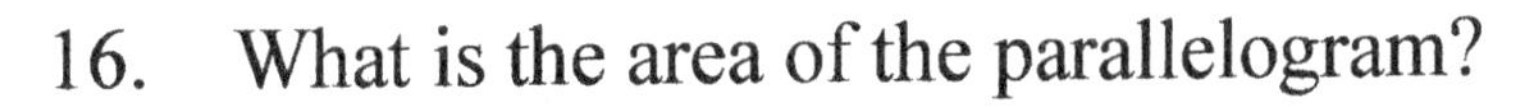

16. What is the area of the parallelogram?

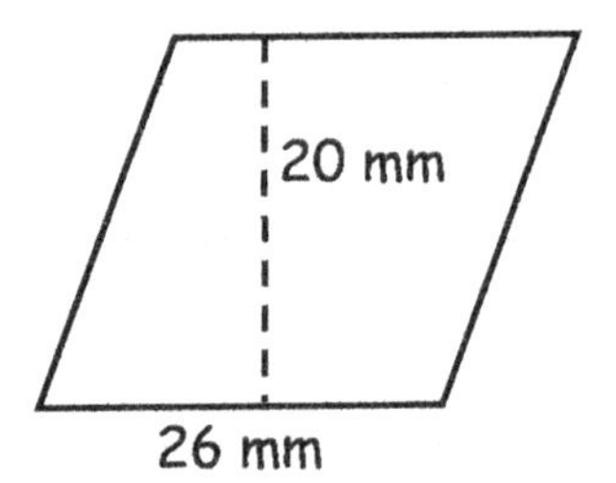

17. Round 21.751 to the nearest hundredth.

18. Convert 400 ounces into pounds.

19. What is the distance around the outside of a circle called?

20. The answer to a division problem is the ______________.

1.	2.	3.	4.
5.	6.	7.	8.
9.	10.	11.	12.
13.	14.	15.	16.
17.	18.	19.	20.

Lesson #125

1. A triangle with two congruent sides is a(n) ________________.

2. 0.578 ◯ 0.56

3. Make a factor tree for 24.

4. $0.007 \times 0.005 = ?$

5. Write the formula for finding the circumference of a circle.

6. Find the area of the triangle.

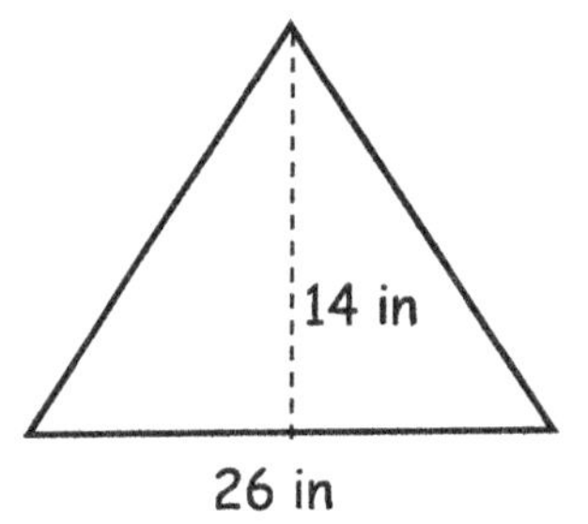

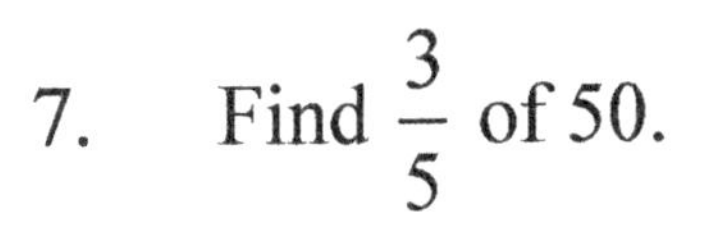

7. Find $\frac{3}{5}$ of 50.

8. $23 \times 36 = ?$

9. If the quotient is 8 and the dividend is 48, what is the divisor?

10. How many centimeters are in 7 meters?

11. $4.5 \div 0.5 = ?$

12. State whether the figure was moved by a rotation, a slide, or a reflection.

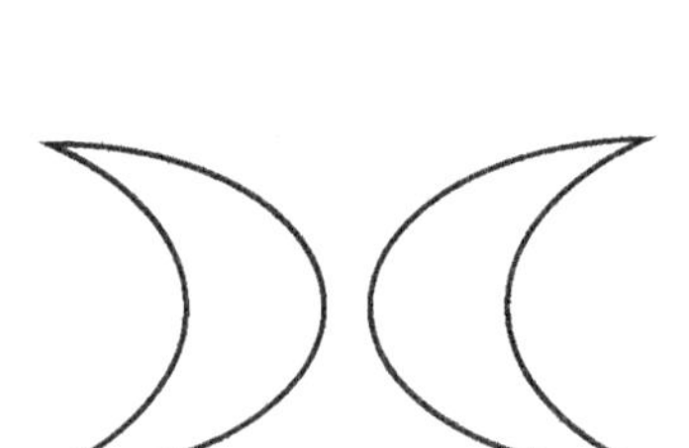

13. $28\frac{1}{6} - 15\frac{5}{6} = ?$

14. Write $\frac{49}{6}$ as a mixed number.

15. Round 3.965 to the nearest hundredth.

16. $2\frac{1}{4} \times 3\frac{1}{9} = ?$

17. $700 - 165 = ?$

18. Which factors of 16 are also factors of 24?

19. $\frac{8}{10} \div \frac{4}{10} = ?$

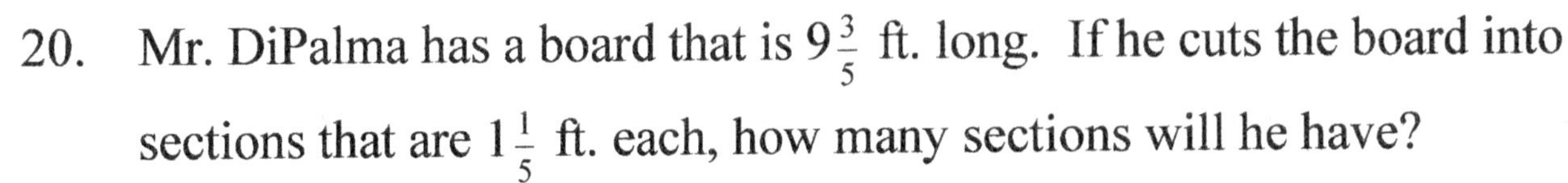

20. Mr. DiPalma has a board that is $9\frac{3}{5}$ ft. long. If he cuts the board into sections that are $1\frac{1}{5}$ ft. each, how many sections will he have?

1.	2.	3.	4.
5.	6.	7.	8.
9.	10.	11.	12.
13.	14.	15.	16.
17.	18.	19.	20.

Lesson #126

1. $0.7 - 0.2179 = ?$

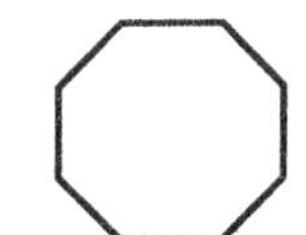

2. What is the name of this shape?

3. Draw a cube. How many faces does it have?

4. If it is 5:20 now, what time was it 6 hours and 10 minutes ago?

5. How many centuries are 800 years?

6. $\frac{5}{6} \times \frac{3}{5} = ?$

7. Write $6\frac{4}{5}$ as an improper fraction.

8. $33 - 21\frac{7}{8} = ?$

9. $0.006 \times 0.04 = ?$

10. Find the average of 2.4, 6.3 and 5.7.

11. Round 356,982,179 to the nearest ten million.

12. $143{,}877 + 659{,}271 = ?$

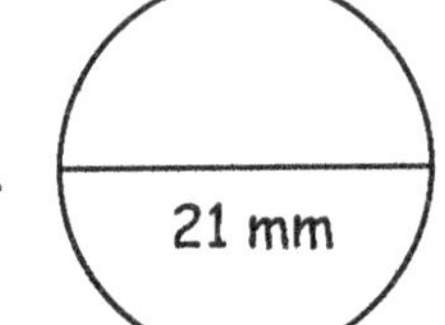

13. Find the circumference of this circle.

14. Find the LCM of 12 and 15.

15. What is the distance across the middle of a circle called?

16. If $9x = 81$, what is the value of x?

17. Write the formula for finding the area of a parallelogram.

18. $6{,}781 \div 9 = ?$

19. Find the probability of rolling a prime number on 1 roll of a die.

20. Myron has to bus tables at a country club party. He is scheduled to work for $1\frac{3}{4}$ hours. Myron will spend $\frac{2}{3}$ of that time washing dishes. How much time will he be washing dishes?

1.	2.	3.	4.
5.	6.	7.	8.
9.	10.	11.	12.
13.	14.	15.	16.
17.	18.	19.	20.

Lesson #127

1. What do you call the distance around the outside of a circle?
2. Find the GCF of 14 and 21.
3. The area of a square is 64 ft^2. What is the length of each side?
4. What time will it be in 9 hours and 25 minutes, if it is 7:10 now?
5. $\frac{5}{8}+\frac{3}{8}=?$

6. Draw a ray.
7. $14-6\frac{5}{7}=?$
8. How many millimeters are 4 meters?
9. $9.5 \div 0.05 = ?$
10. Give the probability of rolling an even number on one roll of a die.
11. The radius of a circle is 35 centimeters. What is the diameter?
12. $0.8 - 0.3295 = ?$
13. Find the area of the parallelogram.

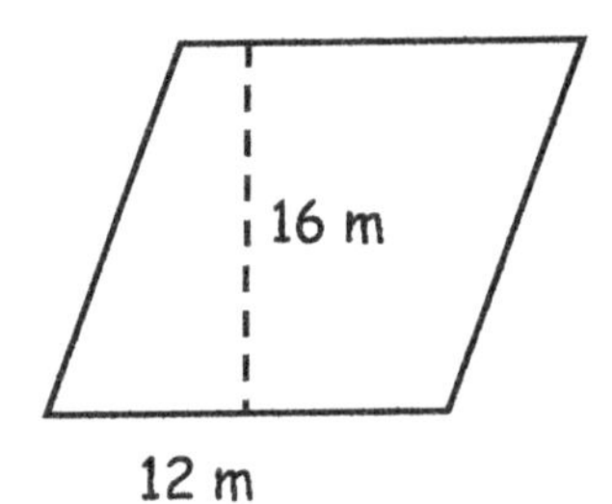

14. Find $\frac{1}{5}$ of 60.
15. Draw two similar pentagons.
16. Write 13.987 using words.
17. $\frac{4}{7}\times\frac{14}{20}=?$
18. Find the median and the mode of 356, 277, 189, 432 and 277.
19. $(20 \div 5) + (10 + 15) = ?$
20. Marsha gets an employee discount at the store where she works. She saves \$10 on each coat plus an extra \$4.25 with today's sale. She also has another coupon for \$5 off. If the coat she wants costs \$85, how much does Marsha pay for her coat (with her discounts)?

1.	2.	3.	4.
5.	6.	7.	8.
9.	10.	11.	12.
13.	14.	15.	16.
17.	18.	19.	20.

Lesson #128

1. Make a factor tree for 30.

2. $\frac{5}{11} \bigcirc \frac{4}{9}$

3. Find the estimated sum of 6,458 and 3,852.

4. $27 \times 42 = ?$

5. Write the formula for finding the area of a triangle.

6. $\frac{9}{4} \div 1\frac{1}{2} = ?$

7. Round 12.7103 to the nearest thousandth.

8. Write 3.412 in words.

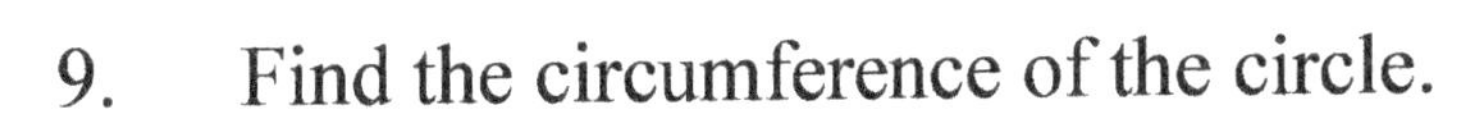

9. Find the circumference of the circle.

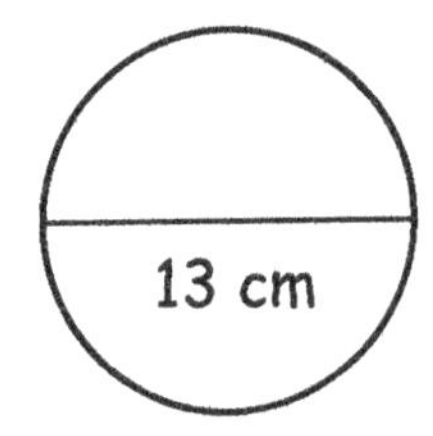

10. $50{,}000 - 22{,}561 = ?$

11. What number is next in this sequence? 145, 154, 163, ...

12. $0.087 \times 0.02 = ?$

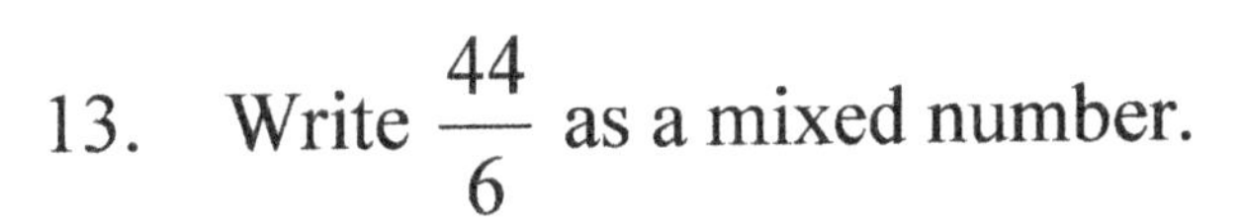

13. Write $\frac{44}{6}$ as a mixed number.

14. $9\frac{2}{7} + 12\frac{1}{3} = ?$

15. How many cups are in 15 pints?

16. $0.3 \bigcirc 0.32$

17. The area of a rectangle is 75 cm^2. If it is 15 cm long, how wide is it?

18. Draw a right angle. How many degrees are in a right angle?

19. Which is greater, 7 minutes or 360 seconds?

20. Thomas goes to summer camp every year. If his parents drive 155 miles to camp, drop him off, and then go back to pick him up in 2 weeks, how many miles will they have traveled?

1.	2.	3.	4.
5.	6.	7.	8.
9.	10.	11.	12.
13.	14.	15.	16.
17.	18.	19.	20.

Lesson #129

1. $64.40 \div 0.04 = ?$

2. Find the median of 336, 317, 329, 373 and 354.

3. Find $\frac{3}{5}$ of 30.

4. Find the area of the triangle.

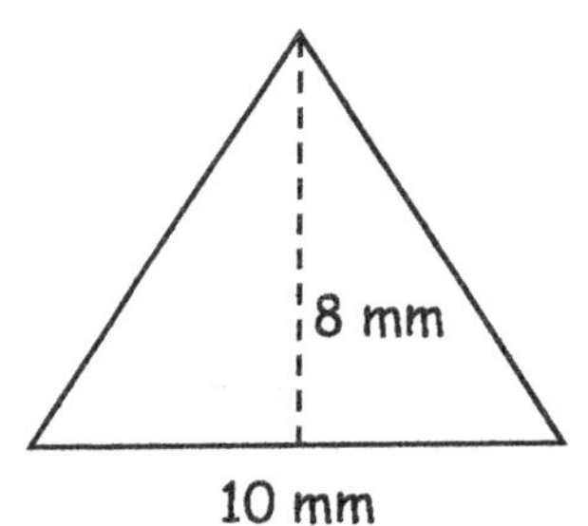

5. $0.82 \times 0.03 = ?$

6. How many inches are in 3 yards?

7. $36 \times 58 = ?$

8. Round 61.82 to the nearest tenth.

9. Is this figure a polygon?

10. $\frac{5}{8} \times \frac{12}{15} = ?$

11. Find the LCM of 12 and 20.

12. $6 - 3\frac{3}{7} = ?$

13. It is 2:25. What time was it 6 hours and 10 minutes ago?

14. $(80 \div 10) + 12 = ?$

15. Find the perimeter of the octagon.

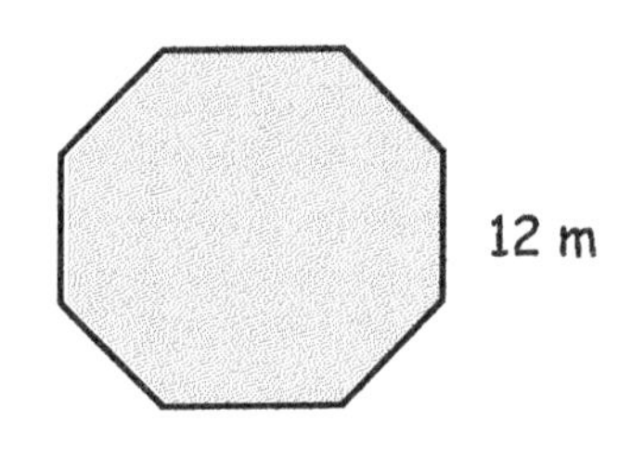

16. $\frac{9}{10} \bigcirc \frac{8}{11}$

17. Write 6.218 in words.

18. **A ratio is a comparison of two numbers. A ratio can be written in 3 forms: word form, fraction form, or ratio form.** Write the three ratio forms: *3:5*, *3 to 5*, $\frac{3}{5}$ in the box.

19. Find the perimeter of the irregular shape.

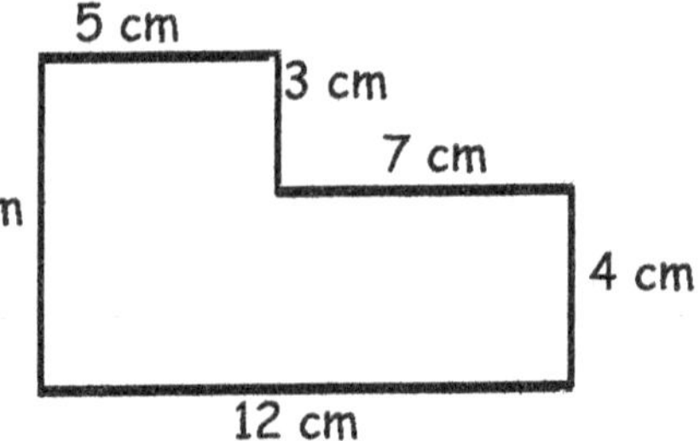

20. $645 \div 3 = ?$

1.	2.	3.	4.
5.	6.	7.	8.
9.	10.	11.	12.
13.	14.	15.	16.
17.	18.	19.	20.

Lesson #130

1. Draw perpendicular lines.

2. 0.07 ◯ 0.078

3. Find the area of a parallelogram whose base is 15 mm and whose height is 7 mm.

4. $0.6 - 0.4271 = ?$

5. Find the probability of rolling an odd number on one roll of a die.

6. $922{,}864 + 758{,}339 = ?$

7. What is the name of this shape?

8. Write $\frac{35}{8}$ as a mixed number.

9. $4.35 \times 0.04 = ?$

10. How many centuries are 800 years?

11. $13\frac{2}{5} + 13\frac{1}{4} = ?$

12. $\frac{7}{8} \times \frac{12}{14} = ?$

13. How many years are 12 decades?

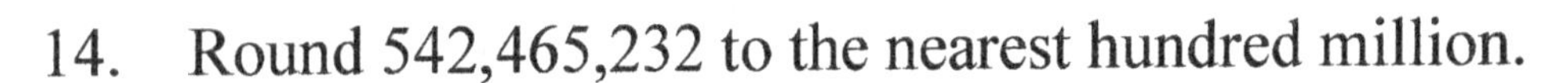

14. Round 542,465,232 to the nearest hundred million.

15. Find the average of 63, 47 and 70.

16. What is the distance around the outside of a circle called?

17. Write $7\frac{4}{5}$ as an improper fraction.

18. $48.63 \div 0.3 = ?$

19. Find the mode and the range of 532, 557, 598, 546 and 557.

20. The cost of a rare coin was $2,000 in 1995, $3,250 in 2000, and $4,500 in 2005. If this pattern continues, what will the price likely be in 2010?

1.	2.	3.	4.
5.	6.	7.	8.
9.	10.	11.	12.
13.	14.	15.	16.
17.	18.	19.	20.

Lesson #131

1. Figures having the same shape, but different size are _______?
2. $\frac{6}{10} \times \frac{4}{12} = ?$
3. Find the GCF and LCM of 8 and 12.
4. If the diameter of a circle is 48 inches, what is the radius?
5. Write the ratio 5:6 two other ways.
6. $0.007 \times 0.008 = ?$
7. Write the time 6 minutes before noon.
8. Find $\frac{2}{3}$ of 90.
9. Draw an acute angle.
10. Find the circumference of the circle.

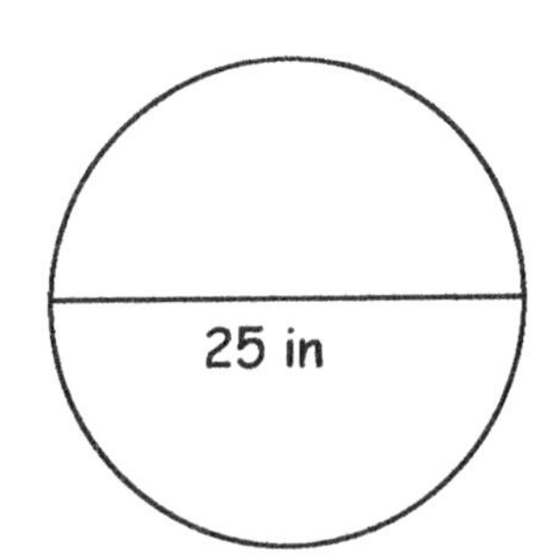

11. $751 - 344 = ?$
12. How many hours are 300 minutes?
13. $\frac{2}{3} \div 2\frac{2}{3} = ?$
14. The ratio of boys to girls in the classroom is 3 to 5. If there are 25 girls, how many boys are in the class?
15. How many pounds are $7\frac{1}{2}$ tons?
16. List the factors of 16.
17. Find the volume of this rectangular prism.

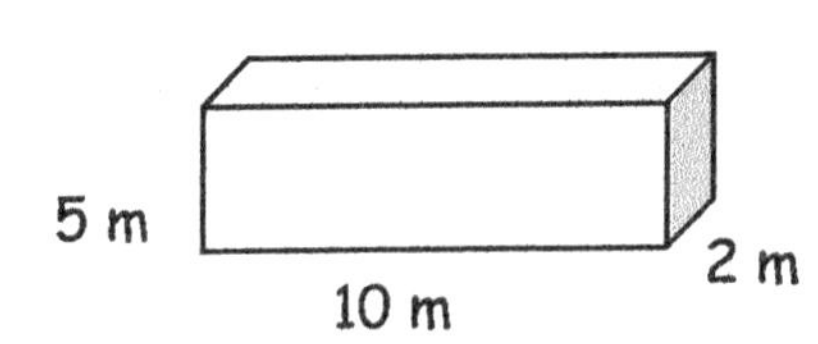

18. Put these decimals in order from greatest to least.
    6.054 6.4 6.045 6.05
19. Which digit is in the millions place in 45,708,692?
20. Is 32 a prime or a composite number?

1.	2.	3.	4.
5.	6.	7.	8.
9.	10.	11.	12.
13.	14.	15.	16.
17.	18.	19.	20.

Lesson #132

1. Draw a straight angle. How many degrees are in a straight angle?

2. $4\frac{1}{2} \times 2\frac{1}{3} = ?$

3. Round 21.536 to the nearest hundredth.

4. $\frac{5}{7} \times \frac{14}{15} = ?$

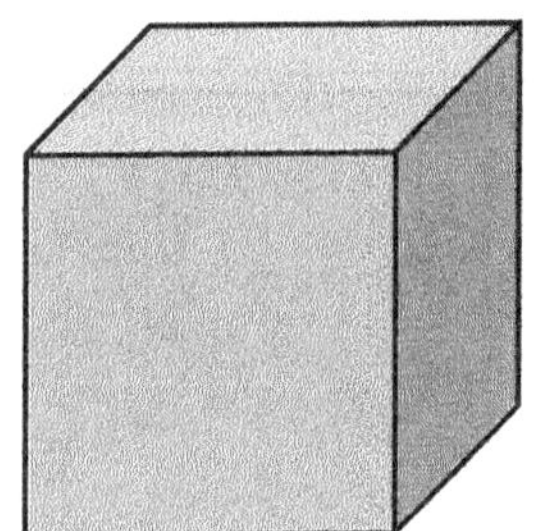

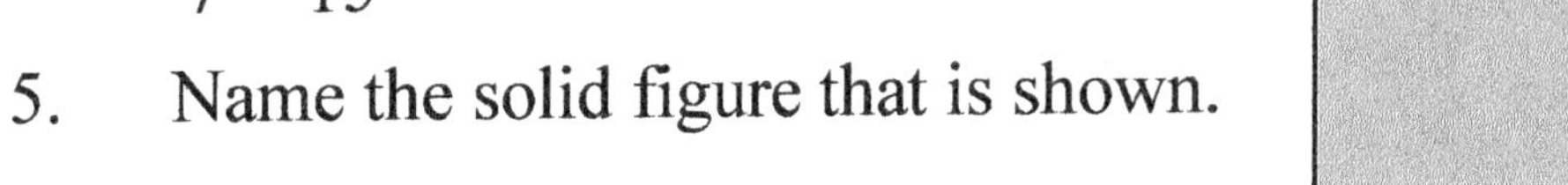

5. Name the solid figure that is shown.

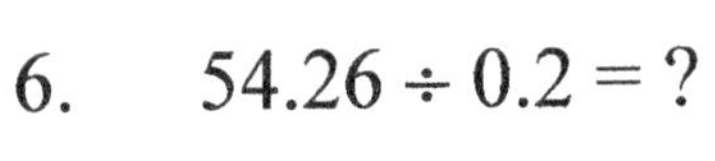

6. $54.26 \div 0.2 = ?$

7. Write 6.3752 in words.

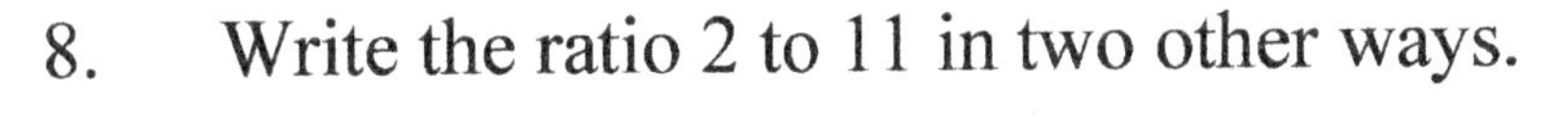

8. Write the ratio 2 to 11 in two other ways.

9. A football team of 30 players ate 20 pizzas. How many pizzas would be needed for 90 players?

10. $\frac{3}{4} \bigcirc \frac{4}{5}$

11. Solve this proportion for x. $\frac{5}{7} = \frac{x}{84}$

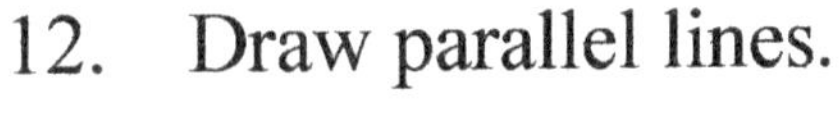

12. Draw parallel lines.

13. $\frac{8}{10} \div \frac{4}{10} = ?$

14. Find the LCM of 9 and 15.

15. How many quarts are in 10 gallons?

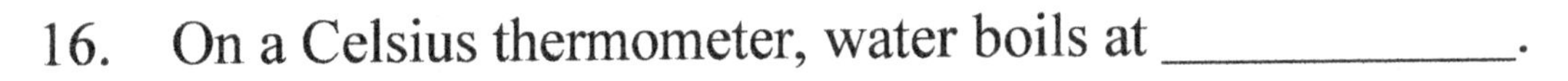

16. On a Celsius thermometer, water boils at ____________.

17. Write *eleven and fifteen hundredths* in decimal form.

18. $43.81 + 8.472 = ?$

19. Closed figures made up of line segments are ______________.

20. $0.005 \bigcirc 0.053$

1.	2.	3.	4.
5.	6.	7.	8.
9.	10.	11.	12.
13.	14.	15.	16.
17.	18.	19.	20.

Lesson #133

1. Numbers that have only 2 factors are ______ numbers.
2. $50{,}000 - 37{,}421 = ?$
3. On the Fahrenheit scale, water freezes at ___________.
4. $3{,}891 \times 6 = ?$
5. Solve the proportion for x. $\frac{8}{12} = \frac{6}{x}$
6. An eight-sided shape is a(n) _______________.
7. What time is it at 40 minutes before noon?
8. $29\frac{3}{7} - 16\frac{6}{7} = ?$
9. Draw a right angle. How many degrees are in a right angle?
10. 9.02 ◯ 9.002
11. Find the GCF of 10 and 25.
12. $0.006 \times 0.03 = ?$
13. Find $\frac{2}{5}$ of 20.
14. Find the average of 65, 30 and 25.
15. $28\frac{3}{5} + 14\frac{1}{2} = ?$

16. What is the probability of rolling a 1 on one roll of a die?
17. Which digit is in the tenths place in 89.076?
18. $\frac{3}{7} \times \frac{14}{21} = ?$
19. Write the formula for finding the circumference of a circle.
20. The seedling grows at the rate of 0.04 inch per day. At this rate, how many inches will the seedling grow in 12 days?

1.	2.	3.	4.
5.	6.	7.	8.
9.	10.	11.	12.
13.	14.	15.	16.
17.	18.	19.	20.

Lesson #134

1. Draw intersecting lines.

2. How many feet are in 2 miles?

3. $16 - 8\frac{2}{5} = ?$

4. On the Celsius scale, at what temperature does water freeze?

5. Make a factor tree for 30.

6. List the first 5 prime numbers.

7. Find the area of this parallelogram.

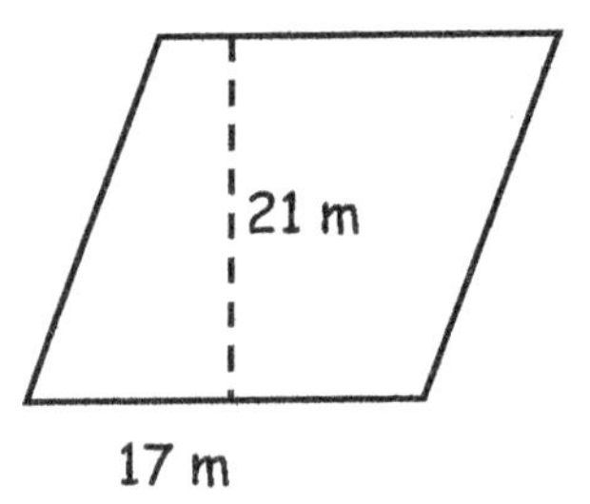

8. 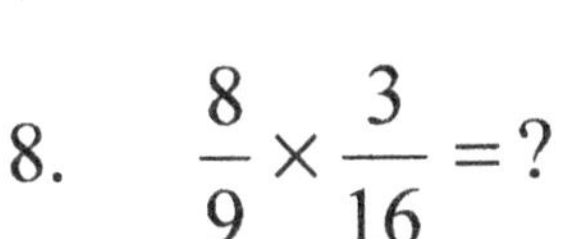 $\frac{8}{9} \times \frac{3}{16} = ?$

9. A triangle with all congruent sides is a(n) __________ triangle.

10. $0.7 - 0.529 = ?$

11. Write $\frac{17}{3}$ as a mixed number.

12. Write the reciprocal of $\frac{3}{7}$.

13. $\frac{9}{12} = \frac{x}{48}$

14. List the factors of 24.

15. Round 15.379 to the nearest hundredth.

16. Find the area of a square if a side measures 12 meters.

17. $98 + 22 + 56 = ?$

18. Write the ratio 7 to 9 two other ways.

19. Rewrite $\frac{10}{25}$ in simplest form.

20. The ratio of blue jays to robins was 6 to 7. If there were 84 robins, how many blue jays were there?

1.	2.	3.	4.
5.	6.	7.	8.
9.	10.	11.	12.
13.	14.	15.	16.
17.	18.	19.	20.

Lesson #135

1. Round 734,294,038 to the nearest hundred million.

2. $\frac{3}{7} - \frac{1}{3} = ?$

3. It is 3:30. What time will it be in 90 minutes?

4. The ratio of trucks to cars on a small stretch of highway was 7 to 12. If there were 105 trucks on the highway, how many cars were there?

5. If $3x = 21$, what is the value of x?

6. Find $\frac{3}{4}$ of 28.

7. Find the area of a rectangle with a length of 18 m and a width of 5 m.

8. How many decades are in 100 years?

9. Find the value of x. $\frac{5}{8} = \frac{45}{x}$

10. $12 - 9\frac{3}{4} = ?$

11. Which is greater, 5,000 pounds or 3 tons?

12. Write 18.921 in words.

13. $36.7 + 94.82 = ?$

14. Is 28 a prime or a composite number?

15. Draw an obtuse angle.

16. Find the circumference of the circle.

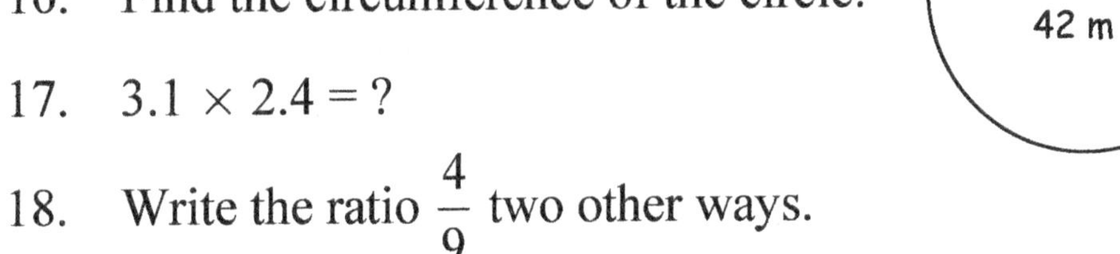

17. $3.1 \times 2.4 = ?$

18. Write the ratio $\frac{4}{9}$ two other ways.

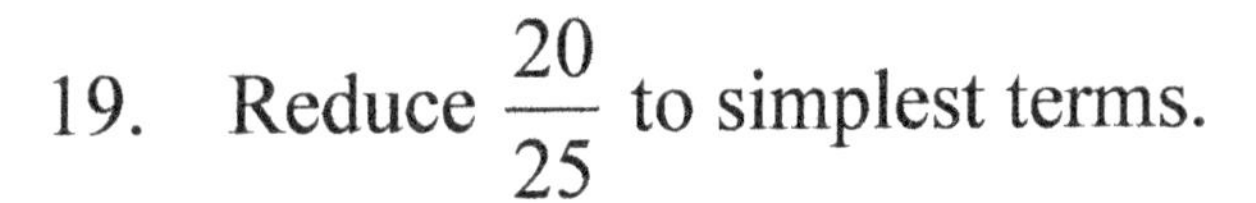

19. Reduce $\frac{20}{25}$ to simplest terms.

20. Write *forty-seven and two hundred fifty-seven thousandths* as a decimal.

1.	2.	3.	4.
5.	6.	7.	8.
9.	10.	11.	12.
13.	14.	15.	16.
17.	18.	19.	20.

Lesson #136

1. Write 4.58 in words.

2. On the Fahrenheit scale, water boils at ______________.

3. $34\frac{1}{8} - 16\frac{5}{8} = ?$

4. $45.05 \div 0.05 = ?$

5. Which digit is in the thousandths place in 24.063?

6. $400 - 126 = ?$

7. Solve the proportion for x. $\frac{3}{5} = \frac{x}{75}$

8. $8.7 - 3.921 = ?$

9. $11\frac{2}{5} + 24\frac{1}{4} = ?$

10. How many cups are in 12 pints?

11. $0.012 \times 0.07 = ?$

12. Figures with the same size and shape are ________________.

13. Write the ratio 8:9 two other ways.

14. Order these decimals from least to greatest. 4.5 4.005 4.506

15. Find the GCF and the LCM of 12 and 18.

16. $156{,}788 + 452{,}794 = ?$

17. Find the area of the parallelogram.

18 cm

13 cm

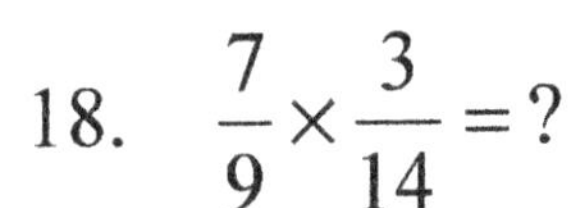

18. $\frac{7}{9} \times \frac{3}{14} = ?$

19. $(5 \times 4) + 25 = ?$

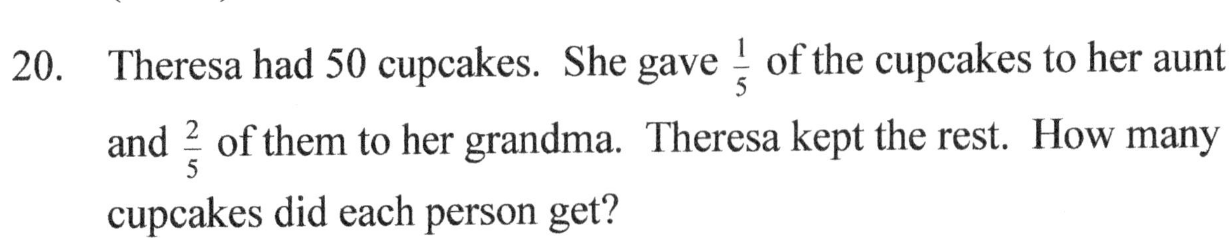

20. Theresa had 50 cupcakes. She gave $\frac{1}{5}$ of the cupcakes to her aunt and $\frac{2}{5}$ of them to her grandma. Theresa kept the rest. How many cupcakes did each person get?

1.	2.	3.	4.
5.	6.	7.	8.
9.	10.	11.	12.
13.	14.	15.	16.
17.	18.	19.	20.

Lesson #137

1. A triangle with no congruent sides is a(n) __________ triangle.

2. How many centuries are between 1650 and 1950?

3. Give the name of this polygon.

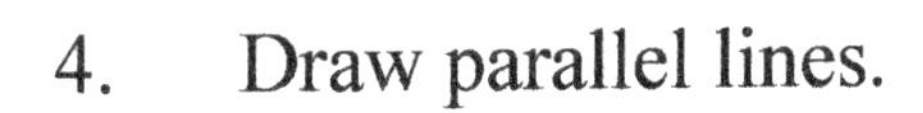

4. Draw parallel lines.

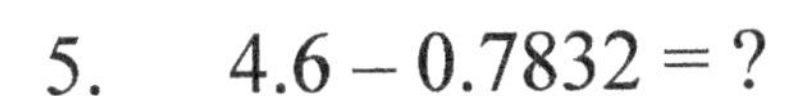

5. $4.6 - 0.7832 = ?$

6. Find $\frac{4}{5}$ of 50.

7. $9\frac{2}{5} + 6\frac{3}{10} = ?$

8. $13 - 5\frac{3}{8} = ?$

9. Make a factor tree for 100.

10. $25 \times 25 = ?$

11. $3 \div 7\frac{1}{2} = ?$

12. How many centimeters are in 15 meters?

13. If $7x = 49$, what is the value of x?

14. How many millimeters are 7 meters?

15. Write the formula for finding the area of a triangle.

16. At what Fahrenheit temperature does water boil?

17. Solve the proportion for x. $\frac{5}{9} = \frac{x}{117}$

18. $\frac{5}{7} \bigcirc \frac{5}{9}$

19. The boy-girl ratio at the dance was 12 to 15. If there were 48 boys, how many girls were at the dance?

20. The area of a square is 36 square feet. How long is each side?

1.	2.	3.	4.
5.	6.	7.	8.
9.	10.	11.	12.
13.	14.	15.	16.
17.	18.	19.	20.

Lesson #138

1. It is 4:15. What time was it 9 hours and 5 minutes ago?
2. Write the name of this shape.

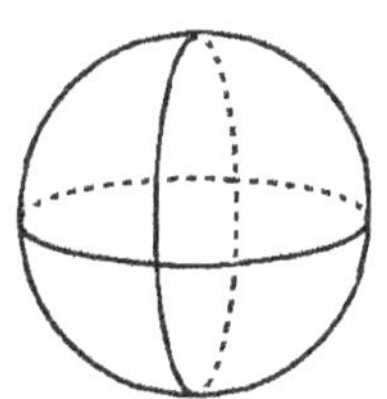

3. $11\frac{1}{5} - 4\frac{4}{5} = ?$

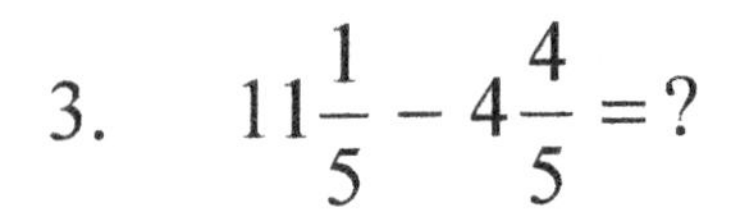

4. Write $5\frac{2}{7}$ as an improper fraction.
5. Closed figures made up of line segments are _______________.
6. Explain how to find the median of a set of numbers.
7. Solve the proportion for x. $\frac{5}{9} = \frac{x}{108}$
8. Find the range of 126, 94, 80, 45 and 26.
9. Draw a ray.
10. $36 \div 0.06 = ?$
11. $80{,}000 - 54{,}396 = ?$
12. Write the ratio *8:9* in two other ways.
13. Find the average of 1.3, 2.0 and 0.81.

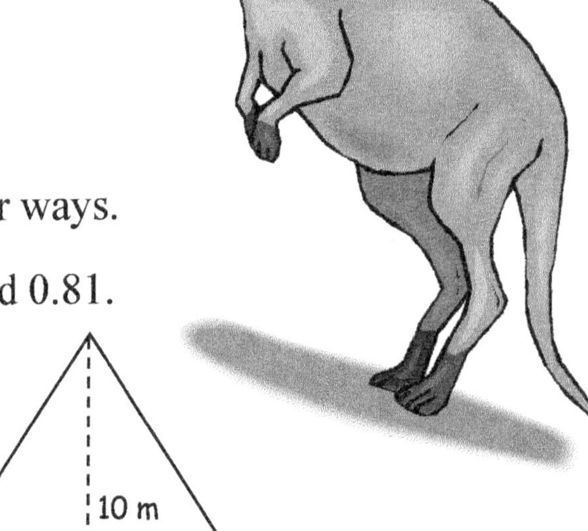

14. $2\frac{1}{4} \div \frac{3}{4} = ?$
15. Find the area of the triangle.

16. $0.005 \times 0.07 = ?$

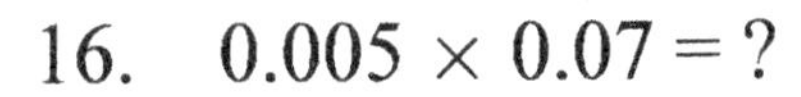

17. The ratio of kangaroo to elephants in the zoo is 5 to 2. If there were 15 kangaroo, how many elephants were in the zoo?
18. $3{,}465 \times 4 = ?$
19. A regular hexagon has a perimeter of 72 in. How long is each side?
20. $965 + 387 = ?$

1.	2.	3.	4.
5.	6.	7.	8.
9.	10.	11.	12.
13.	14.	15.	16.
17.	18.	19.	20.

Lesson #139

1. $0.007 \times 0.04 = ?$

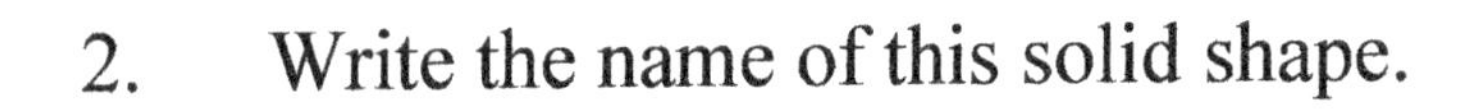

2. Write the name of this solid shape.

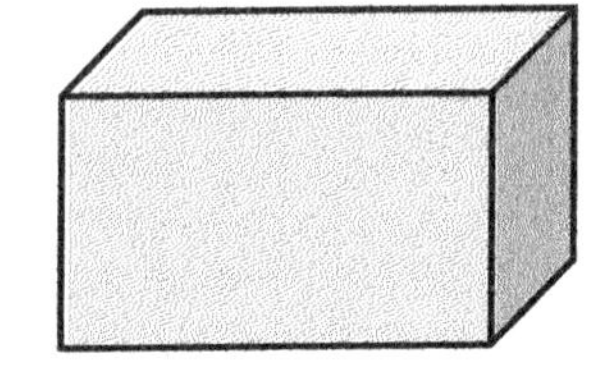

3. List the factors of 20.

4. Round 26.821 to the nearest tenth.

5. What is the answer to a subtraction problem called?

6. $8{,}465 + 2{,}954 = ?$

7. Find $\frac{5}{6}$ of 42.

8. $\frac{5}{8} \times \frac{4}{5} = ?$

9. $0.5 - 0.3271 = ?$

10. How many inches are in 4 feet?

11. Which digit is in the thousandths place in 7.042?

12. Write the ratio 6:7 in two other ways.

13. Round 75,482,163 to the nearest hundred thousand.

14. Solve the proportion for x. $\frac{2}{9} = \frac{x}{180}$

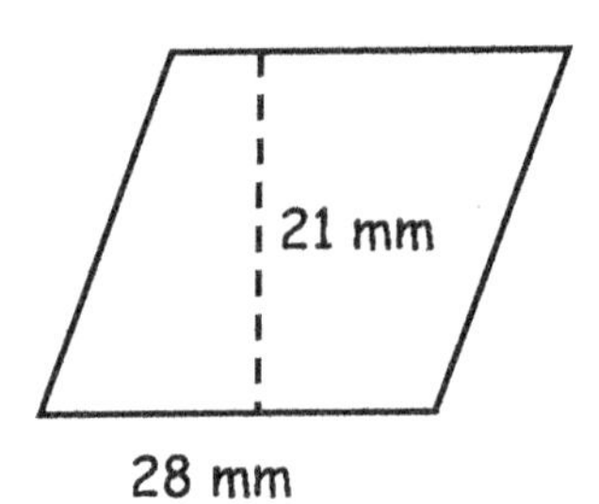

15. Find the area of the parallelogram.

16. Find the GCF of 12 and 24.

17. If $5n = 20$, what is the value of n?

18. What do you call the distance around the outside of a circle?

19. A triangle with 2 congruent sides is a(n) ______ triangle.

20. The ratio of tables to chairs in the banquet hall was 1 to 8. If there were 256 chairs, how many tables were in the hall?

1.	2.	3.	4.
5.	6.	7.	8.
9.	10.	11.	12.
13.	14.	15.	16.
17.	18.	19.	20.

Lesson #140

1. How many degrees are in a right angle?

2. Draw a ray.

3. Write $\frac{18}{4}$ as a mixed number.

4. $0.9 - 0.1894 = ?$

5. Write the formula for finding the circumference of a circle.

6. $\frac{4}{7} \bigcirc \frac{6}{11}$

7. What is the probability of drawing a king out of a deck of 52 cards?

8. On the Fahrenheit temperature scale, water boils at ________.

9. How many inches are in 4 yards?

10. How many gallons are 36 quarts?

11. Write the ratio 8:11 two other ways.

12. Write 71.82 using words.

13. $\frac{6}{10} \div \frac{3}{10} = ?$

14. $3.905 \bigcirc 3.9$

15. $43\frac{1}{2} + 27\frac{5}{8} = ?$

16. Make a factor tree for 28.

17. Round 90,867,552 to the nearest hundred thousand.

18. What do you call the distance around the outside of a circle?

19. $7,890,654 + 3,442,897 = ?$

20. The temperature was 8° at noon. By 11:00 p.m., it had dropped 12°. What was the temperature at 11:00 p.m.?

1.	2.	3.	4.
5.	6.	7.	8.
9.	10.	11.	12.
13.	14.	15.	16.
17.	18.	19.	20.

Intermediate A

Help Pages

Help Pages

Vocabulary

Arithmetic Operations
Difference — the result or answer to a subtraction problem. Example: The difference of 5 and 1 is 4.
Product — the result or answer to a multiplication problem. Example: The product of 5 and 3 is 15.
Quotient — the result or answer to a division problem. Example: The quotient of 8 and 2 is 4.
Sum — the result or answer to an addition problem. Example: The sum of 5 and 2 is 7.

Factors and Multiples
Factors — are multiplied together to get a product. Example: 2 and 3 are factors of 6.
Multiples — can be evenly divided by a number. Example: 5, 10, 15 and 20 are multiples of 5.
Composite Number — a number with more than 2 factors. Example: 10 has factors of 1, 2, 5 and 10. Ten is a composite number.
Prime Number — a number with exactly 2 factors (the number itself and 1). Example: 7 has factors of 1 and 7. Seven is a prime number.
Greatest Common Factor (GCF) — the highest factor that 2 numbers have in common.)See p. 287) Example: The factors of 6 are 1, 2, **3**, and 6. The factors of 9 are 1, **3** and 9. The GCF of 6 and 9 is **3**.
Least Common Multiple (LCM) — the smallest multiple that 2 numbers have in common. (See p. 287) Example: Multiples of 3 are 3, 6, 9, **12**, 15... Multiples of 4 are 4, 8, **12**, 16... The LCM of 3 and 4 is **12**.
Prime Factorization — a number, written as a product of its prime factors. (See p. 287) Example: 140 can be written as 2 x 2 x 5 x 7 or $2^2 \times 5 \times 7$. (All are prime factors of 140.)

Fractions and Decimals
Improper Fraction — a fraction in which the numerator is larger than the denominator. Example: $\frac{9}{4}$
Mixed Number — the sum of a whole number and a fraction. Example: $5\frac{1}{4}$
Reciprocal — a fraction where the numerator and denominator are interchanged. The product of a fraction and its reciprocal is always 1. Example: The reciprocal of $\frac{3}{5}$ is $\frac{5}{3}$. $\frac{3}{5} \times \frac{5}{3} = \frac{15}{15} = 1$
Repeating Decimal — a decimal in which a number or a series of numbers continues on and on. Example: 2.33333333, 4.151515151515, 7.125555555, etc.

Geometry
Acute Angle — an angle measuring less than 90°.
Congruent — figures with the same shape and the same size.
Obtuse Angle — an angle measuring more than 90°.
Right Angle — an angle measuring exactly 90°.
Similar — figures having the same shape, but different size.
Straight Angle — an angle measuring exactly 180°.

Help Pages

Vocabulary (continued)

Geometry — Circles

Circumference — the distance around the outside of a circle.

Diameter — the widest distance across a circle. The diameter always passes through the center.

Radius — the distance from any point on the circle to the center. The radius is half of the diameter.

Geometry — Polygons

Number of Sides	Name	Number of Sides	Name
3	Triangle	7	Heptagon
4	Quadrilateral	8	Octagon
5	Pentagon	9	Nonagon
6	Hexagon	10	Decagon

Geometry — Triangles

Equilateral — a triangle in which all 3 sides have the same length.

Isosceles — a triangle in which 2 sides have the same length.

Scalene — a triangle in which no sides are the same length.

Measurement — Relationships

Volume	Distance
3 teaspoons in a tablespoon	36 inches in a yard
2 cups in a pint	1760 yards in a mile
2 pints in a quart	5280 feet in a mile
4 quarts in a gallon	100 centimeters in a meter
Weight	1000 millimeters in a meter
16 ounces in a pound	**Temperature**
2000 pounds in a ton	0° Celsius - Freezing Point
Time	100°Celsius - Boiling Point
10 years in a decade	32°Fahrenheit - Freezing Point
100 years in a century	212°Fahrenheit - Boiling Point

Ratio and Proportion

Proportion — a statement that two ratios (or fractions) are equal. Example: $\frac{1}{2} = \frac{3}{6}$

Ratio — a comparison of two numbers by division; a ratio may look like a fraction. (See p. 297)
Example: $\frac{2}{5}$ or 2 to 5 or 2:5.

Help Pages

Vocabulary (continued)

Statistics

Mean — the average of a group of numbers. The mean is found by finding the sum of a group of numbers and then dividing the sum by the number of members in the group.

Example: The average of 12, 18, 26, 17 and 22 is **19**. $\frac{12+18+26+17+22}{5}=\frac{95}{5}=19$

Median — the middle value in a group of numbers. The median is found by listing the numbers in order from least to greatest, and finding the one that is in the middle of the list. If there is an even number of members in the group, the median is the average of the two middle numbers.

Example: The median of 14, 17, 24, 11 and 26 is **17**. 11, 14, (17), 24, 26

The median of 77, 93, 85, 95, 70 and 81 is **83**. 70, 77, (81, 85), 93, 95 $\frac{81+85}{2}=83$

Mode — the number that occurs most often in a group of numbers. The mode is found by counting how many times each number occurs in the list. The number that occurs more than any other is the mode. Some groups of numbers have more than one mode.

Example: The mode of 77, (93), 85, (93), 77, 81, (93) and 71 is **93**. (93 occurs more than the others.)

Place Value

Whole Numbers

8, 9 6 3, 2 7 1, 4 0 5

8	9	6	3	2	7	1	4	0	5
Billions	Hundred Millions	Ten Millions	Millions	Hundred Thousands	Ten Thousands	Thousands	Hundreds	Tens	Ones

The number above is read: eight billion, nine hundred sixty-three million, two hundred seventy-one thousand, four hundred five.

Decimal Numbers

1 7 8 . 6 4 0 5 9 2

1	7	8	.	6	4	0	5	9	2
Hundreds	Tens	Ones	*Decimal Point*	Tenths	Hundredths	Thousandths	Ten-thousandths	Hundred-thousandths	Millionths

The number above is read: one hundred seventy-eight and six hundred forty thousand, five hundred ninety-two millionths.

Help Pages

Solved Examples

Factors & Multiples

The **Prime Factorization** of a number is when a number is written as a product of its prime factors. A factor tree is helpful in finding the prime factors of a number.

Example: Use a factor tree to find the prime factors of 45.

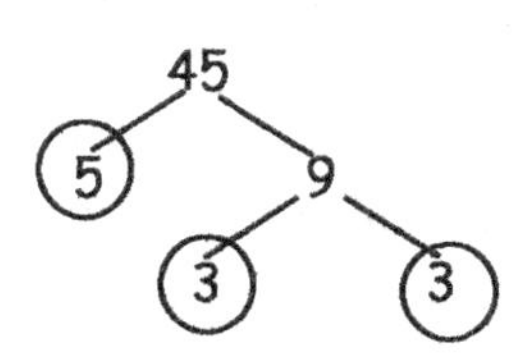

1. Find any 2 factors of 45 (5 and 9).
2. If a factor is prime, circle it. If a factor is not prime, find 2 factors of it.
3. Continue until all factors are prime.
4. In the final answer, the prime factors are listed in order, least to greatest, using exponents when needed.

The prime factorization of 45 is $3 \times 3 \times 5$ or $3^2 \times 5$.

The **Greatest Common Factor (GCF)** is the largest factor that 2 numbers have in common.

Example: Find the Greatest Common Factor of 32 and 40.

The factors of 32 are 1, 2, 4, (8), 16, 32.

The factors of 40 are 1, 2, 4, 5, (8), 10, 20, 40.

1. First list the factors of each number.
2. Find the largest number that is in both lists.

The GCF of 32 and 40 is **8**.

The **Least Common Multiple (LCM)** is the smallest multiple that two numbers have in common. The prime factors of the numbers can be useful in finding the LCM.

Example: Find the Least Common Multiple of 16 and 24.

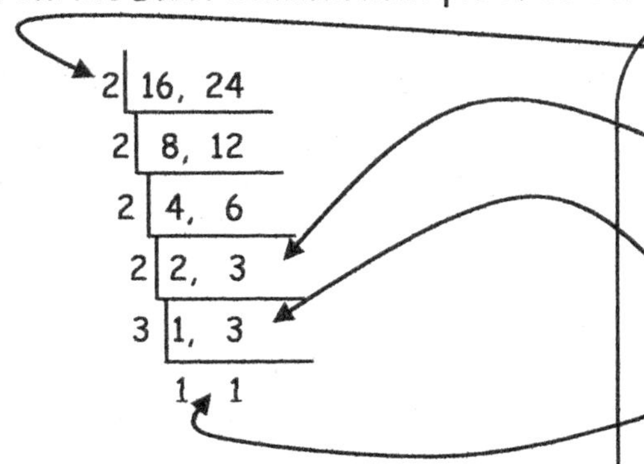

1. If any of the numbers are even, factor out a 2.
2. Continue factoring out 2 until all numbers left are odd.
3. If the prime number cannot be divided evenly into the number, simply bring the number down.
4. Once you are left with all 1's at the bottom, you're finished!
5. Multiply all of the prime numbers (on the left side of the bracket) together to find the Least Common Multiple.

The LCM is 2 x 2 x 2 x 2 x 3 or **48**.

Fractions

Changing from an improper fraction to a mixed number.

Example: Change the improper fraction, $\frac{5}{2}$, to a mixed number.

$\frac{5}{2}$ (five halves) means $5 \div 2$.

So, $\frac{5}{2}$ is equal to 2 wholes and 1 half or $2\frac{1}{2}$.

$$\begin{array}{r} 2 \text{ wholes} \\ 2\overline{)5} \\ \underline{-4} \\ 1 \text{ half} \end{array}$$

Help Pages

Solved Examples

Fractions (continued)

Changing from a mixed number to an improper fraction.

Example: Change the mixed number, $7\frac{1}{4}$, to an improper fraction.

1. You're going to make a new fraction. To find the numerator of the new fraction, multiply the whole number by the denominator, and add the numerator.
2. Keep the same denominator in your new fraction as you had in the mixed number.

$7\frac{1}{4}$ $7 \times 4 = 28.$ $28 + 1 =$ **29**.

The new numerator is 29.

Keep the same denominator, 4.

The new fraction is $\frac{29}{4}$.

$7\frac{1}{4}$ is equal to $\frac{29}{4}$.

Equivalent Fractions are 2 fractions that are equal to each other. Usually you will be finding a missing numerator or denominator.

Example: Find a fraction that is equivalent to $\frac{4}{5}$ and has a denominator of 35.

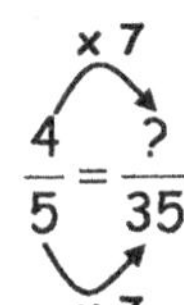

1. Ask yourself, "What did I do to 5 to get 35?" (Multiply by 7.)
2. Whatever you did in the denominator, you also must do in the numerator. $4 \times 7 = 28$. The missing numerator is 28.

So, $\frac{4}{5}$ is equivalent to $\frac{28}{35}$.

Example: Find a fraction that is equivalent to $\frac{4}{5}$ and has a numerator of 24.

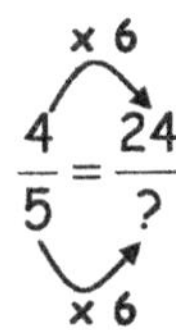

1. Ask yourself, "What did I do to 4 to get 24?" (Multiply by 6.)
2. Whatever you did in the numerator, you also must do in the denominator. $5 \times 6 = 30$. The missing denominator is 30.

So, $\frac{4}{5}$ is equivalent to $\frac{24}{30}$.

Comparing Fractions means looking at 2 or more fractions and determining if they are equal, if one is greater than (>) the other, or if one is less than (<) the other. A simple way to compare fractions is by cross-multiplying, using the steps below.

Examples: Compare these fractions. Use the correct symbol. $\frac{8}{9} \bigcirc \frac{3}{4}$ $\frac{7}{9} \bigcirc \frac{6}{7}$

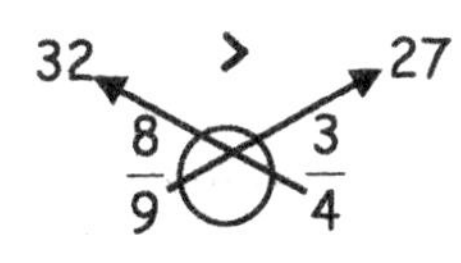

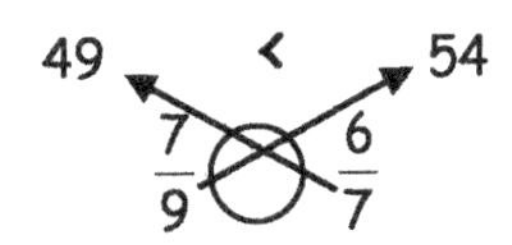

1. Begin with the denominator on the left and multiply by the opposite numerator. Put the answer (product) above the right side. $(9 \times 3 = 27)$
2. Cross-multiply the denominator on the right and the opposite numerator and put the answer above the left side.
3. Compare the two answers and insert the correct symbol.

   HINT: **Always** multiply diagonally **upwards**!

So, $\frac{8}{9} > \frac{3}{4}$ and $\frac{7}{9} < \frac{6}{7}$.

Help Pages

Solved Examples

Fractions (continued)

To **add (or subtract) fractions with the same denominator**, simply add (or subtract) the numerators, keeping the same denominator.

Examples: $\frac{3}{5}+\frac{1}{5}=\frac{4}{5}$

$\frac{8}{9}-\frac{1}{9}=\frac{7}{9}$

To **add mixed numbers**, follow a process similar to the one you used with fractions. If the sum is an improper fraction, be sure to simplify it.

Example:
$$\begin{array}{r} 1\frac{2}{5} \\ +1\frac{4}{5} \\ \hline 2\frac{6}{5} \end{array}$$

$2\frac{6}{5}$ is improper. $\frac{6}{5}$ can be rewritten as $1\frac{1}{5}$.

So, $2\frac{6}{5}$ is $2 + 1\frac{1}{5} = 3\frac{1}{5}$.

When **adding fractions that have different denominators**, you need to change the fractions so they have a common denominator before they can be added.

Finding the **Least Common Denominator (LCD):**

The LCD of the fractions is the same as the Least Common Multiple of the denominators. Sometimes, the LCD will be the product of the denominators.

Example: Find the sum of $\frac{3}{8}$ and $\frac{1}{12}$.

$$\begin{array}{r} \frac{3}{8}=\frac{9}{24} \\ +\frac{1}{12}=\frac{2}{24} \\ \hline \frac{11}{24} \end{array}$$

1. First, find the LCM of 8 and 12.
2. The LCM of 8 and 12 is 24. This is also the LCD of these 2 fractions.
3. Find an equivalent fraction for each that has a denominator of 24.
4. When they have a common denominator, the fractions can be added.

```
2| 8,12
2| 4, 6
2| 2,3
3| 1,3
   1,1
```

$2\times2\times2\times3=24$

The LCM is 24.

Example: Add $\frac{1}{4}$ and $\frac{1}{5}$.

$$\begin{array}{r} \frac{1}{4}=\frac{5}{20} \\ +\frac{1}{5}=\frac{4}{20} \\ \hline \frac{9}{20} \end{array}$$

$4\times5=20$ The LCM is 20.

When **adding mixed numbers with unlike denominators**, follow a process similar to the one you used with fractions (above). Be sure to put your answer in simplest form.

Example: Find the sum of $6\frac{3}{7}$ and $5\frac{2}{3}$.

$$\begin{array}{r} 6\frac{3}{7}=6\frac{9}{21} \\ +5\frac{2}{3}=5\frac{14}{21} \\ \hline 11\frac{23}{21} \end{array}$$

(improper)

$\frac{23}{21}=1\frac{2}{21}+11=12\frac{2}{21}$

1. Find the LCD.
2. Find the missing numerators.
3. Add the whole numbers, then add the fractions.
4. Make sure your answer is in simplest form.

Help Pages

Solved Examples

Fractions (continued)

When **subtracting numbers with unlike denominators**, follow a process similar to the one you used when adding fractions. Be sure to put your answer in simplest form.

Examples: Find the difference of $\frac{3}{4}$ and $\frac{2}{5}$.

$$\begin{array}{r} \frac{3}{4} = \frac{15}{20} \\ -\frac{2}{5} = \frac{8}{20} \\ \hline \frac{7}{20} \end{array}$$

1. Find the LCD just as you did when adding fractions.
2. Find the missing numerators.
3. Subtract the numerators and keep the common denominator.
4. Make sure your answer is in simplest form.

Subtract $\frac{1}{16}$ from $\frac{3}{8}$.

$$\begin{array}{r} \frac{3}{8} = \frac{6}{16} \\ -\frac{1}{16} = \frac{1}{16} \\ \hline \frac{5}{16} \end{array}$$

When **subtracting mixed numbers with unlike denominators**, follow a process similar to the one you used when adding mixed numbers. Be sure to put your answer in simplest form.

Example: Subtract $4\frac{2}{5}$ from $8\frac{9}{10}$.

1. Find the LCD.
2. Find the missing numerators.
3. Subtract and simplify your answer.

$$\begin{array}{r} 8\frac{9}{10} = 8\frac{9}{10} \\ -4\frac{2}{5} = 4\frac{4}{10} \\ \hline 4\frac{5}{10} = 4\frac{1}{2} \end{array}$$

Sometimes when subtracting mixed numbers, you may need to regroup. If the numerator of the top fraction is smaller than the numerator of the bottom fraction, you must borrow from your whole number.

Example: Subtract $5\frac{5}{6}$ from $9\frac{1}{4}$.

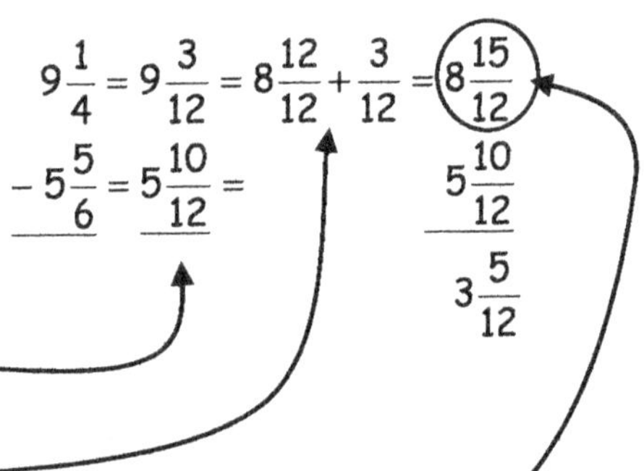

1. Find the LCD.
2. Find the missing numerators.
3. Because you can't subtract 10 from 3, you need to borrow from the whole number.
4. Rename the whole number as a mixed number using the common denominator.
5. Add the 2 fractions to get an improper fraction.
6. Subtract the whole numbers and the fractions and simplify your answer.

More examples:

$$\begin{array}{r} 8\frac{1}{2} = 8\frac{2}{4} = 7\frac{4}{4} + \frac{2}{4} = 7\frac{6}{4} \\ -4\frac{3}{4} = 4\frac{3}{4} = \quad 4\frac{3}{4} \\ \hline 3\frac{3}{4} \end{array}$$

$$\begin{array}{r} 10\frac{1}{5} = 10\frac{4}{20} = 9\frac{20}{20} + \frac{4}{20} = 9\frac{24}{20} \\ -\ 6\frac{3}{4} = 6\frac{15}{20} = \quad 6\frac{15}{20} \\ \hline 3\frac{9}{20} \end{array}$$

Help Pages

Solved Examples

Fractions (continued)

To **multiply fractions**, simply multiply the numerators together to get the numerator of the product. Then multiply the denominators together to get the denominator of the product. Make sure your answer is in simplest form.

Examples: Multiply $\frac{3}{5}$ by $\frac{2}{3}$.

$\frac{3}{5} \times \frac{2}{3} = \frac{6}{15} = \frac{2}{5}$

1. Multiply the numerators.
2. Multiply the denominators.
3. Simplify your answer.

Multiply $\frac{5}{8}$ by $\frac{4}{5}$.

$\frac{5}{8} \times \frac{4}{5} = \frac{20}{40} = \frac{1}{2}$

Sometimes you can use cancelling when multiplying fractions. Let's look at the examples again.

$\frac{\cancel{3}^{1}}{5} \times \frac{2}{\cancel{3}_{1}} = \frac{2}{5}$

The 3's have a common factor — 3. Divide both of them by 3. Since, $3 \div 3 = 1$, we cross out the 3's and write 1's in their place.

Now, multiply the fractions. In the numerator, $1 \times 2 = 2$. In the denominator, $5 \times 1 = 5$.

The answer is $\frac{2}{5}$.

1. Are there any numbers in the numerator and the denominator that have common factors?
2. If so, cross out the numbers, divide both by that factor, and write the quotient.
3. Then, multiply the fractions as described above, using the quotients instead of the original numbers.

$\frac{\cancel{5}^{1}}{{}_{2}\cancel{8}} \times \frac{\cancel{4}^{1}}{\cancel{5}_{1}} = \frac{1}{2}$

As in the other example, the 5's can be cancelled. But here, the 4 and the 8 also have a common factor — 4. $8 \div 4 = 2$ and $4 \div 4 = 1$. After cancelling both of these, you can multiply the fractions.

REMEMBER: You can cancel up and down or diagonally, but NEVER sideways!

When **multiplying mixed numbers**, you must first change them into improper fractions.

Examples: Multiply $2\frac{1}{4}$ by $3\frac{1}{9}$.

$2\frac{1}{4} \times 3\frac{1}{9} =$

$\frac{\cancel{9}^{1}}{{}_{1}\cancel{4}} \times \frac{\cancel{28}^{7}}{\cancel{9}_{1}} = \frac{7}{1} = 7$

1. Change each mixed number to an improper fraction.
2. Cancel wherever you can.
3. Multiply the fractions.
4. Put your answer in simplest form.

Multiply $3\frac{1}{8}$ by 4.

$3\frac{1}{8} \times 4 =$

$\frac{25}{{}_{2}\cancel{8}} \times \frac{\cancel{4}^{1}}{1} = \frac{25}{2} = 12\frac{1}{2}$

To **divide fractions**, you must take the reciprocal of the 2nd fraction, and then multiply that reciprocal by the 1st fraction. Don't forget to simplify your answer!

Examples: Divide $\frac{1}{2}$ by $\frac{7}{12}$.

$\frac{1}{2} \div \frac{7}{12} =$

$\frac{1}{{}_{1}\cancel{2}} \times \frac{\cancel{12}^{6}}{7} = \frac{6}{7}$

1. Keep the 1st fraction as it is.
2. Write the reciprocal of the 2nd fraction.
3. Change the sign to multiplication.
4. Cancel if you can and multiply.
5. Simplify your answer.

Divide $\frac{7}{8}$ by $\frac{3}{4}$.

$\frac{7}{8} \div \frac{3}{4} =$

$\frac{7}{{}_{2}\cancel{8}} \times \frac{\cancel{4}^{1}}{3} = \frac{7}{6} = 1\frac{1}{6}$

Help Pages

Solved Examples

Fractions (continued)

When **dividing mixed numbers**, you must first change them into improper fractions.

Example: Divide $1\frac{1}{4}$ by $3\frac{1}{2}$.

$$1\frac{1}{4} \div 3\frac{1}{2} =$$
$$\frac{5}{4} \div \frac{7}{2} =$$
$$\frac{5}{\cancel{4}_2} \times \frac{\cancel{2}^1}{7} = \frac{5}{14}$$

1. Change each mixed number to an improper fraction.
2. Keep the 1st fraction as it is.
3. Write the reciprocal of the 2nd fraction.
4. Change the sign to multiplication.
5. Cancel if you can and multiply.
6. Simplify your answer.

Decimals

When we **compare decimals**, we are looking at two or more decimal numbers and deciding which has the smaller or larger value. We sometimes compare by placing them in order from least to greatest or from greatest to least. Another way to compare is to use the symbols for "less than" (<), "greater than" (>) or "equal to" (=).

Example: Order these numbers from least to greatest. 0.561 0.506 0.165

1. Write the numbers in a column, lining up the decimal points.
2. Write zeroes, if necessary, so all have the same number of digits.
3. Begin on the left and compare the digits.

0.561
0.506
0.165

Since they all have 3 digits, we don't need to add zeroes. Beginning on the left, the five's are equal, but the one is less, so 0.165 is the smallest. Then, look at the next digit. The zero is less than the six, so 0.506 is next smallest.

So, in order from least to greatest:

0.165, 0.506, 0.561

Example: Place these numbers in order from greatest to least. 0.44 0.463 0.045

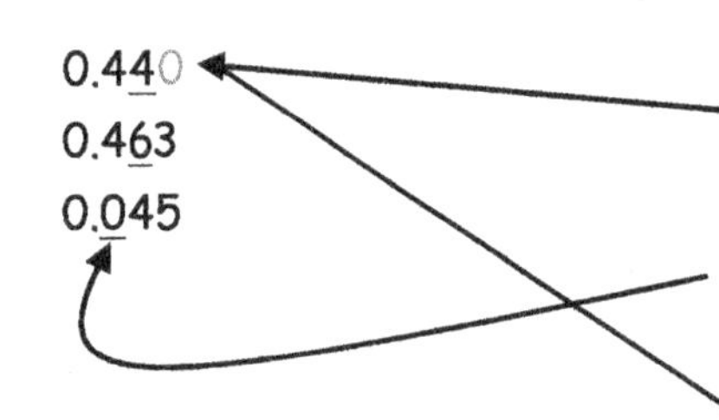

After lining up the numbers, we must add a zero to 0.44 to make them all have the same number of digits.

Beginning on the left, the zero is smaller than the four's, so 0.045 is the smallest.

Look at the next digit. The four is smaller than the six, so 0.440 is the next smallest.

In order from greatest to least: 0.463, 0.440, 0.045

Help Pages

Solved Examples

Decimals (continued)

When we **round decimals**, we are approximating them. This means we end the decimal at a certain place value and we decide if it's closer to the next higher number (round up) or to the next lower number (keep the same). It might be helpful to look at the decimal place-value chart on p. 286.

Example: Round 0.574 to the tenths place.

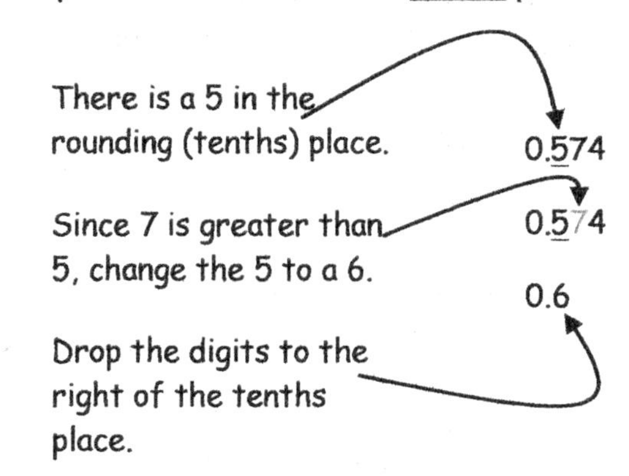

1. Identify the number in the rounding place.
2. Look at the digit to its right.
3. If the digit is 5 or greater, increase the number in the rounding place by 1. If the digit is less than 5, keep the number in the rounding place the same.
4. Drop all digits to the right of the rounding place.

Example: Round 2.783 to the nearest hundredth.

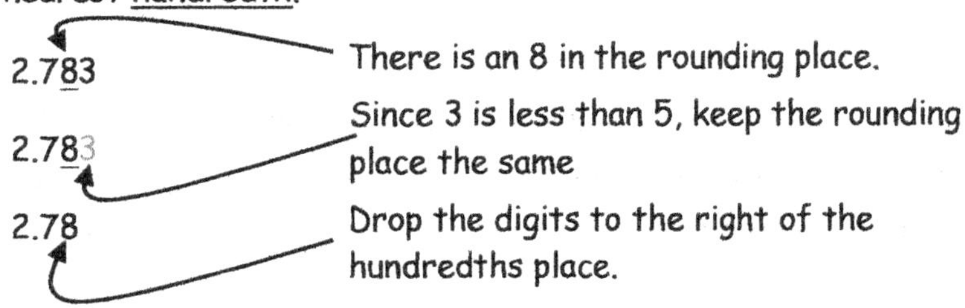

Adding and subtracting decimals is very similar to adding or subtracting whole numbers. The main difference is that you have to line-up the decimal points in the numbers before you begin.

Examples: Find the sum of 3.14 and 1.2.

```
  3.14
+ 1.20
  4.34
```

Add 55.1, 6.472 and 18.33.

```
  55.100
   6.472
 +18.330
  79.902
```

1. Line up the decimal points. Add zeroes as needed.
2. Add (or subtract) the decimals.
3. Add (or subtract) the whole numbers.
4. Bring the decimal point straight down.

Examples: Subtract 3.7 from 9.3.

```
  9.3
- 3.7
  5.6
```

Find the difference of 4.1 and 2.88.

```
  4.10
- 2.88
  1.22
```

Help Pages

Solved Examples

Decimals (continued)

When **multiplying a decimal by a whole number**, the process is similar to multiplying whole numbers.

Examples: Multiply 3.42 by 4.

3.42 → 2 decimal places
× 4 → 0 decimal places
13.68 → Place decimal point so there are 2 decimal places.

1. Line up the numbers on the right.
2. Multiply. Ignore the decimal point.
3. Place the decimal point in the product. (The total number of decimal places in the product must equal the total number of decimal places in the factors.)

Find the product of 2.3 and 2.

2.3 → 1 decimal place
× 2 → 0 decimal places
4.6 → Place decimal point so there is 1 decimal place.

The process for **multiplying two decimal numbers** is a lot like what we just did above.

Examples: Multiply 0.4 by 0.6.

0.4 → 1 decimal place
× 0.6 → 1 decimal place
0.24 → Place decimal point so there are 2 decimal places.

Find the product of 2.67 and 0.3.

2.67 → 2 decimal places
× 0.3 → 1 decimal place
0.801 → Place decimal point so there are 3 decimal places.

Sometimes it is necessary to add **zeroes in the product** as placeholders in order to have the correct number of decimal places.

Example: Multiply 0.03 by 0.4.

0.03 → 2 decimal places
× 0.4 → 1 decimal place
0.012 → Place decimal point so there are 3 decimal places.

We had to add a zero in front of the 12 so that we could have 3 decimal places in the product.

The process for **dividing a decimal number by a whole number** is similar to dividing whole numbers.

Examples: Divide 6.4 by 8.

```
  0.8
8)6.4
 -6 4
    0
```

1. Set up the problem for long division.
2. Place the decimal point in the quotient directly above the decimal point in the dividend.
3. Divide. Add zeroes as placeholders if necessary. (See examples below.)

Find the quotient of 20.7 and 3.

```
   6.9
3)20.7
 -18
   27
  -27
    0
```

Examples: Divide 4.5 by 6.

Find the quotient of 3.5 and 4.

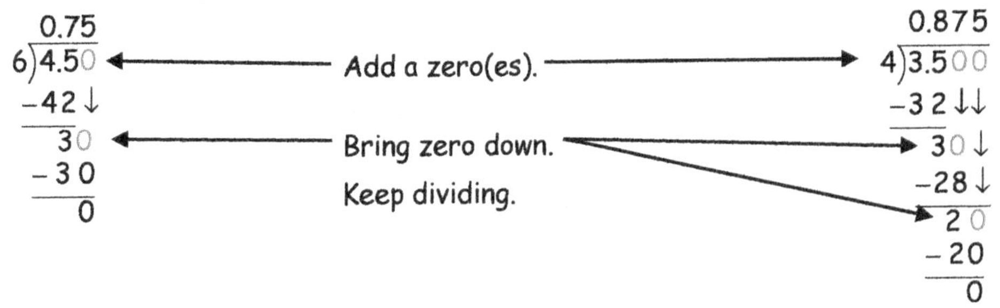

Help Pages

Solved Examples

Decimals (continued)

When dividing decimals the remainder is not always zero. Sometimes, the division continues on and on and the remainder begins to repeat itself. When this happens the quotient is called a **repeating decimal**.

Examples: Divide 2 by 3. Divide 10 by 11.

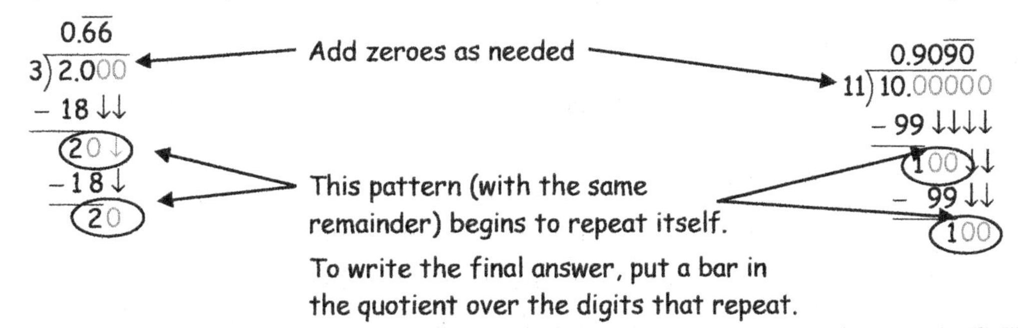

The process for **dividing a decimal number by a decimal number** is similar to other long division that you have done. The main difference is that we have to move the decimal point in both the dividend and the divisor the same number of places to the right.

Example: Divide 1.8 by 0.3. Divide 0.385 by 0.05.

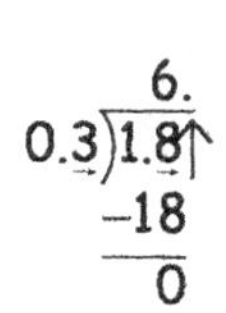

1. Change the divisor to a whole number by moving the decimal point as many places to the right as needed.
2. Move the decimal in the dividend the same number of places to the right as you did in the divisor.
3. Put the decimal point in the quotient directly above the decimal point in the dividend.
4. Divide.

```
      7.7
0.05)0.385
    –35
      35
     –35
       0
```

Geometry

Finding the **area of a parallelogram** is similar to finding the area of any other quadrilateral. The area of the figure is equal to the length of its base multiplied by the height of the figure.

Area of parallelogram = base × height or $A = b \times h$

Example: Find the area of the parallelogram below.

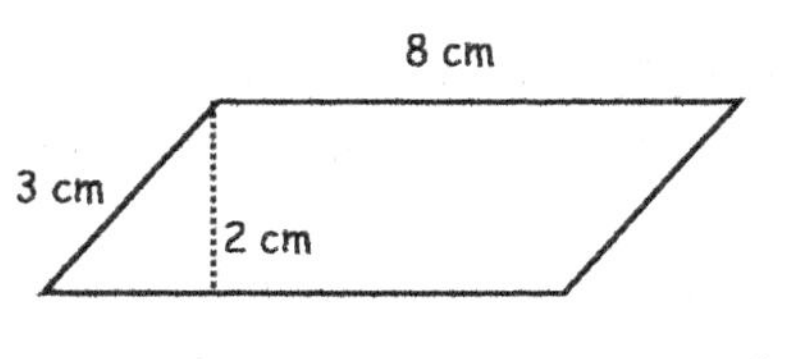

So, $A = 8\text{ cm} \times 2\text{ cm} = 16\text{ cm}^2$.

1. Find the length of the base. (8 cm)
2. Find the height. (It is 2 cm. The height is always straight up and down - never slanted.)
3. Multiply to find the area. (16 cm^2)

Help Pages

Solved Examples

Geometry (continued)

To find the **area of a triangle**, it is helpful to recognize that any triangle is exactly half of a parallelogram.

The whole figure is a parallelogram.

Half of the whole figure is a triangle.

So, the triangle's area is equal to half of the product of the base and the height.

$$\text{Area of triangle} = \frac{1}{2}(\text{base} \times \text{height}) \quad \text{or} \quad A = \frac{1}{2}bh \quad \text{or} \quad A = \frac{bh}{2}$$

Examples: Find the area of the triangles below.

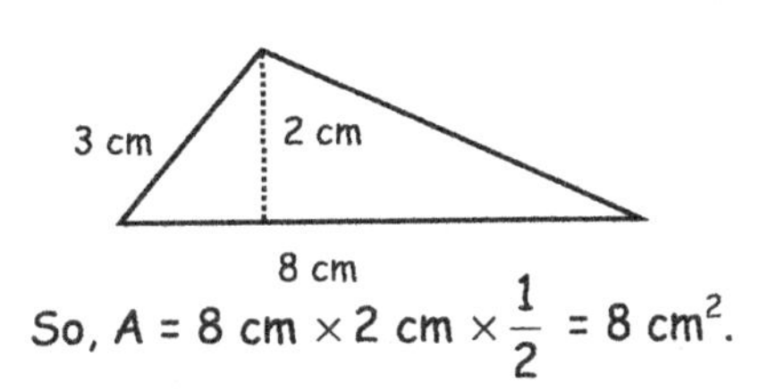

So, $A = 8\text{ cm} \times 2\text{ cm} \times \frac{1}{2} = 8\text{ cm}^2$.

1. Find the length of the base. (8 cm)
2. Find the height. (It is 2 cm. The height is always straight up and down – never slanted.)
3. Multiply them together and divide by 2 to find the area. (8 cm^2)

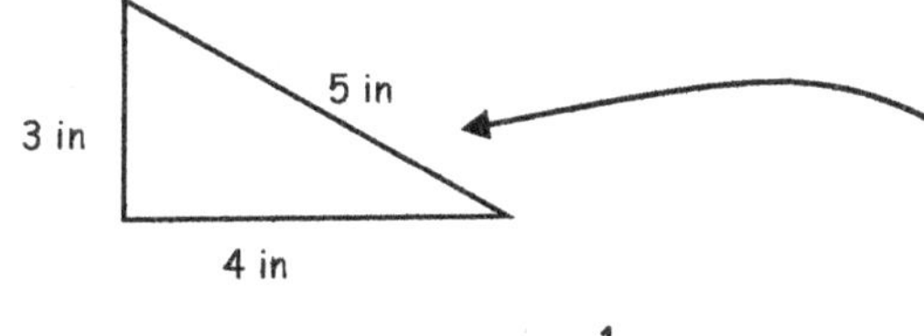

The base of this triangle is 4 inches long. Its height is 3 inches. (Remember the height is always straight up and down!)

So, $A = 4\text{ in} \times 3\text{ in} \times \frac{1}{2} = 6\text{ in}^2$.

The **circumference of a circle** is the distance around the outside of the circle. Before you can find the circumference of a circle you must know either its radius or its diameter. Also, you must know the value of the constant, pi (π). $\pi = 3.14$ (rounded to the nearest hundredth).

Once you have this information, the circumference can be found by multiplying the diameter by pi.

$$\text{Circumference} = \pi \times \text{diameter} \quad \text{or} \quad C = \pi d$$

Examples: Find the circumference of the circles below.

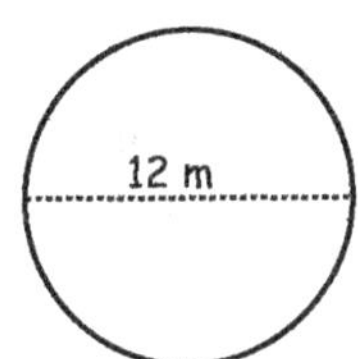

1. Find the length of the diameter. (12 m)
2. Multiply the diameter by π. ($12\text{ m} \times 3.14$).
3. The product is the circumference. (37.68 m)

So, $C = 12\text{ m} \times 3.14 = 37.68\text{ m}$.

Sometimes the radius of a circle is given instead of the diameter. Remember, the radius of any circle is exactly half of the diameter. If a circle has a radius of 3 feet, its diameter is 6 feet.

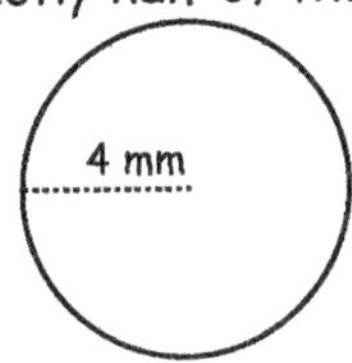

Since the radius is 4 mm, the diameter must be 8 mm.

Multiply the diameter by π. ($8\text{ mm} \times 3.14$).

The product is the circumference. (25.12 mm)

So, $C = 8\text{ mm} \times 3.14 = 25.12\text{ mm}$.

Help Pages

Solved Examples

Ratio and Proportion

A **ratio** is used to compare two numbers. There are three ways to write a ratio comparing 5 and 7:

1. Word form ➡ 5 to 7
2. Fraction form ➡ $\frac{5}{7}$
3. Ratio form ➡ 5 : 7

You must make sure that all ratios are written in simplest form. (Just like fractions!!)

A **proportion** is a statement showing that two ratios are equal to each other. There are two ways to solve a proportion when a number is missing.

1. One way to solve a proportion is already familiar to you. You can use the equivalent fraction method.

$$\frac{5}{8} = \frac{n}{64} \quad (\times 8)$$

$n = 40.$

So, $\frac{5}{8} = \frac{40}{64}$.

2. Another way to solve a proportion is by using cross-products.

To use Cross-Products:

1. Multiply downward on each diagonal.
2. Make the product of each diagonal equal to each other.
3. Solve for the missing variable.

$$\frac{14}{20} = \frac{21}{n}$$

$$20 \times 21 = 14 \times n$$

$$420 = 14n$$

$$\frac{420}{14} = \frac{14n}{14}$$

$$30 = n$$

So, $\frac{14}{20} = \frac{21}{30}$.

Who Knows???

Degrees in a right angle? ....(90)
A straight angle? ....(180)
Angle greater than 90°? ....(obtuse)
Less than 90°? ....(acute)
Sides in a quadrilateral? ....(4)
Sides in an octagon?.................(8)
Sides in a hexagon? ....(6)
Sides in a pentagon? ....(5)
Sides in a heptagon? ....(7)
Sides in a nonagon? ....(9)
Sides in a decagon? .... (10)
Inches in a yard? ....(36)
Yards in a mile? ....(1,760)
Feet in a mile? ....(5,280)
Centimeters in a meter? ....(100)
Teaspoons in a tablespoon? ...(3)
Ounces in a pound? ....(16)
Pounds in a ton?........................(2,000)
Cups in a pint? ....(2)
Pints in a quart? ....(2)
Quarts in a gallon? ....(4)
Millimeters in a meter? ....(1,000)
Years in a century? ....(100)
Years in a decade? ....(10)
Celsius freezing? ....(0°C)
Celsius boiling? ....(100°C)
Fahrenheit freezing? ....(32°F)

Fahrenheit boiling? ....(212°F)
Number with only 2 factors? (prime)
Perimeter? ....(add the sides)
Area of rectangle? ......(length x width)
Volume or prism? (length x width x height)
Area of parallelogram?.. (base x height)
Area of triangle? ......($\frac{1}{2}$ base x height)
Area of trapezoid..($\frac{\text{base} + \text{base}}{2} \times$ height)
Area of a circle? ....(πr^2)
Circumference of a circle? ....($d\pi$)
Triangle with no sides equal? (scalene)
Triangle with 3 sides equal? ....(equilateral)
Triangle with 2 sides equal? ....(isosceles)
Distance across the middle of a circle? ....(diameter)
Half of the diameter? .... (radius)
Figures with the same size and shape? ....(congruent)
Figures with same shape, different sizes? ....(similar)
Number occurring most often? (mode)
Middle number? ....(median)
Answer in addition? ....(sum)
Answer in division? .... (quotient)
Answer in subtraction? ...(difference)
Answer in multiplication? .... (product)